Preface

It is an obvious fact now that the Internet is becoming part of our life. More and more contents are delivered over the Internet. As the heterogeneity in the Internet increases, content providers are considering adaptive content delivery to achieve better user satisfaction. However, so far there are still no thorough study of how contents are delivered over the Internet and how we can achieve better adaptive content delivery.

In this book, we try to illustrate the Internet content delivery mechanism. And based on this mechanism we propose an adaptive content delivery framework which can greatly help Internet Service Providers and Internet Content Providers to achieve quality-based content delivery service. This book can be used as an introduction for Internet content based technology researchers, and can also be used as a reference book for graduate students.

This book is the refined wisdom from the Institute of Information Security Engineering, Shanghai Jiao Tong University. We appreciate all of our colleagues for their great help in this book. And we would also express our sincere appreciation towards Shanghai Jiao Tong University Press. Without their help, we would never have this book published so smoothly.

Xiang Li
Jianhua Li
Feb. 10th, 2010

Contents

1

Introduction

1.1 Background

The Internet today is everywhere in people's life. With its advantages of multimedia and user interactivity, it is becoming one of the dominant media. Nowadays, it is not only providing all kinds of information, but also a platform for education, business, and entertainment. E-learning, E-business, etc. are no longer abstract concepts, but concrete applications that all people can enjoy. As Internet becomes more and more important in our lives, people expect good service quality from it.

The variety of Internet browsers has never been as diversified as today. Besides traditional PCs, more and more new devices such as PDAs, hand-held PCs, hand phones, etc. are being widely used as browsing tools. And with the people coming from different parts of the world, the Internet is facing a wide variety of users with different access speeds (from 28.8 Kbps modem to T1/T2/T3), language requirement, culture, etc. Under such condition, the "good-quality service" is no longer a simple concept. We believe that there are three issues which are fundamental to the provisioning of quality-based web content delivery. They are (i) retrieval latency, (ii) best-fit pervasive Internet access, and (iii) content access control and policy enforcement.

Retrieval latency is directly related to a surfer's satisfaction towards a website. When the Internet is used as a media for business and news publishing, retrieval latency must be kept low. It is a usual misunderstanding that the only way to improve retrieval latency is to increase the network bandwidth. While this argument is valid, there are other factors that affect the retrieval latency of web browsing. Best-fit pervasive Internet access is to address the browsers' variation and requirements. Since browsing devices might differ so much in their network, hardware, and software condition, they should be served with different versions and qualities of the web content that can best fit their requirements. With surfers of different cultures and age groups all coming into the Internet, content access control and policy enforcement are absolutely necessary to make sure that the resource usage and the surfers are well protected.

There are suggested solutions to address one or two of these three issues. With the traditional structure of client-server architecture, the proposed solutions are often broken down into server side solution and client side solution.

On the web server side, content publishers can make their content more friendly for web delivery. To achieve fast delivery, content publishers can use new data formats that can efficiently decrease the requirement of network bandwidth. Image formats like progressive JPEG and JPEG 2000 can improve the perceived latency of surfers. Video formats like RM, and WMV allow video streaming over the congested Internet. To achieve content customization, one common solution on the web server side is to put multiple copies of one object to fit different user preferences. This solution is very popular to provide multilingual web pages according to the preference information of the visitors' browsers. The main advantage of this solution is that since content publishers own the content, they should know how to customize their content and achieve better quality of the delivered content. However, since their major target is to serve the whole Internet, it will be quite impractical for them to customize the content for minority groups. Very often, the major focus of web sites is to provide content availability. It is quite difficult for them to understand how their content can be optimized for delivery. Furthermore, due to the conflict of interest, it is inappropriate to have access control and content filtering on the web server side.

On the client side, most solutions are in the form of plug-ins for browsers or special software to optimize the OS network operations. For example, a lot of people combine content browsers with some software plug-in like Norton AntiVirus to block the virus or Cyber Patrol to block pornographic materials. This plug-in approach is modular and flexible to fulfill many requirements. However, such solutions might not be efficient in the Internet environment. If every PC needs to install the same plug-in, it might be more cost effective to have a centralized solution for them to share. Distributed solution brings trouble to maintenance and administration. And some applications such as image transcoding to save network bandwidth might not be appropriate to be done in the browser's plug-in approach.

In the Internet environment, people are looking for centralized, one-to-many solution. Such solution is expected to be cost-effective and scalable. This brings out the solution as the network intermediary servers. Researchers believe that by turning the traditional passive web intermediary servers into active ones, the new requirements of content delivery can be fulfilled. By "active", we mean that the network has the intelligence and authority to manipulate data and to make decision on how content should be delivered in the network. The concept of active web intermediary server was first suggested in active network research. Later, researchers find that it is a good solution to the heterogeneity requirement of web content delivery network. Experimental systems such as Pythia and TrenSend were built to explore the feasibility of such active web intermediary server approach. Industry also notices the great potentials of this approach. As a result, several protocols such as I-CAP, SOAP and OPES are defined for web intermediary applications. Some web intermediary server based applications including anti-virus gateway, automatic language translation gateway, and content filtering gateway are widely discussed today.

1.2 Challenges

Though the direction of active web intermediary server is good to achieve the requirements for "quality-service" web content delivery, there are several questions to be answered before solutions can be practically implemented into the network. To build an application in the network, especially in places such as web intermediary proxy, performance is the most important factor for success. Network itself is expected to have high throughput. And data streaming and real time processing are the basic requirements for network applications, which makes the high performance requirement so critical to the feasibility of active web intermediary servers.

The performance requirement actually leads us to a more fundamental question: what does performance mean in web content delivery? Traditional performance study on web content delivery focuses on the object retrieval latency. We argue that this is not sufficient to reflect the satisfaction level of web surfers. First, in real life, a basic web request is a web page instead of a specific object alone. Therefore, just measuring the object retrieval latency might not be enough to show the visual effect of the network delay. Second, and more importantly, there exist retrieval dependencies among objects within the same web page. Measuring the object's downloading time alone cannot reveal such dependencies. Finally, the situation is made even more complicated with the parallel fetching of web objects. Therefore we need a new performance measuring method to better understand the performance of web content delivery.

Another big challenge is the real-time content transformation itself. An active web intermediary performs transformation on the data that streams through it. Since it needs to be done in a way that the high performance requirement can be met, such transformation needs to be designed with tight constraints, which are quite different from those in normal standalone applications. A good example is the availability of streaming data for content transformation without buffering in the network.

Other challenges include scalable system framework for active network intermediaries and its system requirements in their implementation.

1.3 Research Topics

To meet the challenges mentioned in Section 1.2, several research topics are of our interest. The first one is the performance measurement model for web content delivery. Traditionally, only the object retrieval time is used as an indicator for content delivery. However, the visual effect of the whole page downloading, the retrieval latency, and the inter-object dependencies make the object-based measurement approach insufficient. What we need is a model that can illustrate the inter-object relationship within a page and can show the place where the network delay of a page downloading is introduced.

With this model, we can get a clearer view of the content delivery mechanism on the Internet. This knowledge can also provide hints on where and how the performance of web content delivery can be improved.

Another topic is about the real-time content transformation in the web intermediary server. As transformation in the web intermediate server should not sacrifice the server's high performance, we need to have a good understanding of the constraints of the operation environment. In web content delivery, data is streaming over the network. This means a network node tries to pass the data to the next node without data buffering. However, when an active web intermediary is introduced, this streaming mechanism might be affected. While some applications can be done without holding the transmitted data in the network, there are a lot of applications that need to buffer some or even the whole object data. Currently, not much research is done on performance difference between streaming data delivery and buffered data delivery. However, the difference between them affects the performance of web content delivery significantly when object dependencies and pipelining are considered. No study is done on abstracting the content transformation model from the viewpoint of the network performance. But to develop high performance active intermediary applications, such general transformation model that takes the network's data streaming constraint into consideration is needed; it can provide hints on the algorithm design for web intermediary applications.

To make active web intermediaries feasible and practical, a generic system framework is needed. With a scalable system framework, different applications can be added in smoothly. This system framework needs to consider all possible situations of network-based content transformation in web intermediaries. Furthermore, if it can be combined with the basic cache function of web proxy, it will be ideal since data reuse has already been proven to be an efficient way to reduce network delay and system resource. Together with the specification of the system requirements, the system framework can give researchers and developers insight into how such web intermediaries can meet the requirements of quality-based web content delivery.

1.4 Focus of This Book

In this book, we first propose a chunk-level latency dependence model (C-LDM) to describe the retrieval dependencies of objects within a web page. According to the HTTP protocol, data is streamed through the network chunk by chunk. Hence, the chunk level can be taken as the basic network transmission level for the HTTP protocol. This model not only illustrates object dependencies in web content delivery, but also shows how web page structure contributes to the retrieval latency of a web page. With understanding from both the browser view and proxy view on web page retrieval time, we can draw the conclusion that for a typical network environment, the retrieval dependencies among data chunks of a web page template (e.g. HTML object of the page) and its embedded objects are the dominant factors of the total page retrieval time.

Once we find out that the object retrieval dependence is a major factor for web page retrieval delay, we propose two mechanisms to improve the web page retrieval by reducing the object dependencies in a page. One proposed solution is the Object Declaration mechanism. With content provider's help, all objects embedded in a web page can be declared at the very beginning of the page. Then the dependencies between the basic page template and its embedded objects are almost reduced to the minimum. Another solution is the page structure table (or PST) mechanism. Proxy as the web intermediary can record the structure of the retrieved web pages; the dependencies among objects can then be reduced by reusing such information. Each method is proven to be effective to improve web page retrieval. Depending on the number of embedded objects in a web page and the cacheability of the objects, performance improvement ranging from 3% to 18% in page download time can be obtained.

In an active web intermediary server, or simply active proxy server, the core concept is the real-time content transformation. Transformation in these servers achieves the purpose of value-added services. In this book, we do a detailed analysis on the modes of real-time content transformation in web intermediary servers. To differentiate between streaming and whole file buffering, we propose the streaming mode and the buffering mode for real-time content transformation in the network. In web content delivery, since chunk is the basic data unit for transmission, we further break down the streaming modes into byte streaming and chunk streaming. We first define a very general basic content transformation model. Then we map different parameter combinations of this content transformation into three modes. Since there exists big performance difference among these three modes, this mapping is valuable as it provides insight information on how the transformation in web intermediary servers should be designed.

When we talk about the actual deployment for this kind of active web intermediary servers, we need not only the theoretical study of the performance, but also the concrete system architecture. In this book, we propose a 4-stage AXForm Framework for web intermediaries. The data flow of a typical web intermediary server (or active proxy server) is well studied. Then we define four stages to further segment a web transaction. Due to the unique properties of the available data, input and output, and their relation with the proxy cache, each stage has its own appropriate transformation application domain. Moreover, besides the unique properties of each stage, there are also common system requirements for building such web intermediaries. We find out that issues such as handling working space, new process, collecting client/server information, etc. are important system considerations for their actual implementation and deployment.

1.5 Book Outline

The outline of this book is as follows. Chapter 2 is the literature review on the related research work. Chapter 3 defines a Chunk-Level Latency Dependence Model for web content delivery. With this model, people can better understand the performance of web content delivery mechanism. Chapter 4 discusses how to accelerate content delivery based on the Chunk-Level Latency Dependence Model defined in Chapter 3. Chapter 5 discusses the implications of different modes for implementing the "active proxy". Chapter 6 presents the 4-stage transformation framework for active web intermediaries and the design considerations for its system implementation.

2

Related Work

2.1 New Challenges to Web Content Delivery

It is generally agreed that the Internet has already become an important media of our daily lives. With its interactive and multimedia abilities, the Internet has an even greater potential than any of the current media such as television or telephone. It is no longer just a media for personal communication and information dissemination, it is also a platform for education, business, and entertainment. This can be reflected by the fact that despite the fluctuation of e-commerce applications, the numbers of Internet users and web pages published on the Internet keep increasing.

With various kinds of applications being explored on this media, there are always three fundamental issues of content delivery that every Internet infrastructure needs to address. They are (i) retrieval latency (or "world wide wait" problem), (ii) best-fit pervasive Internet access, and (iii) content access control and policy enforcement.

Retrieval latency perceived by a client user is an important performance measurement parameter for every web-based application. In 1998 about 10%~25% of e-commerce transactions were aborted owing to long response delay, which was translated to about 1.9 billion dollars loss of revenue (Wilson 1999). Although network infrastructure and bandwidth availability have been constantly improved in the last decade, they are still unable to meet the increasing network bandwidth demand for multimedia data and the "real-time" expectation of client users. The increasing cost gap between network bandwidth and machine hardware makes this situation worse.

The demand for best-fit pervasive Internet access originates from the growing popularity of personal devices used to access the Internet. These devices include handphones, personal data assists (PDAs), games stations, notebooks, and desktop PCs. With a wide variation of their computation power and display capability, together with their associated different network bandwidth availability, it is a big challenge for a content/service provider with one source to offer the most cost-effective, best-fit presentation to his global client users with different needs. In addition, the changing client's preference and network dynamics make this situation more complicated to handle.

Content access control and policy enforcement is another important concern in the deployment of Internet infrastructures and applications. From the content side, the flooding of undesirable information on the Internet makes efficient content filtering and blocking essential for Internet deployment (especially in schools and at home). Efficient information dissemination on the Internet also results in a great demand for effective mechanisms to protect the copyright of digital data. On the client user side, when an enterprise deploys an Internet infrastructure, accountability of Internet usage is important and effective enforcement mechanism for the enterprise's Internet related policies is needed. Due to its history of development, the original approach that the Internet adopts for these control and enforcement problems is self-regulatory. However, with the penetration of the Internet into various aspects of our daily life and business world, this approach is found to be very limited and inefficient for obvious reasons.

To address these three fundamental aspects of quality-based web content delivery, researchers turn to intelligent network proxy instead of browser or server for solution at the application level. Since all web traffic needs to pass through the network gateway, proxy solution is a one-to-many, cost-effective solution with centralized management. It does not directly depend on the number of machines (in the form of clients or servers) behind it. It is cost-effective because of its dedicated hardware design for content delivery and one-to-many nature. Policy enforcement can be made easier because it does not require collaboration from the client users or web servers. More important, however, is the fact that there are services that should be done more appropriately in the network proxy than in the browser or the server. Some good examples are the local advertisement uploading and content personalization with maximum data reuse. For a web server to handle these applications, it needs to mark the requested object as non-cacheable. This is highly undesirable because it will imply the disabling of the proven effective web caching technology.

The implementation of intelligence into the network proxy for real-time content transformation and adaptation turns the network into the "active" mode because the network is now involving in the decision making on content creation, presentation, and modification. With its great potential to provide better quality for web services and browsing experience, active network is becoming a new direction for content delivery and pervasive computing. Since this book is focused on active network research, we would like to give detailed literature review on various research efforts related to active network and its associated proxy systems. On the technology side, the survey will cover basic proxy caching, image transcoding, multimedia data format, system framework, markup language, and protocols. On the system side, it will describe the major proxy-based adaptive content delivery frameworks and systems that are proposed and implemented in the past few years.

2.2 Overview of Active Network

Traditionally, a network is mainly focused on the connectivity and delivery speed between a server and a client. It is considered as "passive" because whatever data enters into the network at one end, the same data content will go out from the other end of the network. There should not be any data manipulation or modification done in the network.

However, as more applications with diversified requirements are put onto the web, researchers and developers start to realize that intelligence in the network gateway is becoming an essential element to determine the success and efficiency of web applications. This starts with the centralized content filtering and blocking proxy approach (Tennenhouse and Wetherall 1996; Psounis 1999) to replace the inefficient, self-regulatory PICS (Platform for Internet Content Selection) approach (PICS) for pornographic and offensive content access control. Pervasive Internet access is the next driving force for network intelligence as one version of the content needs to serve wide variations of clients with different device hardware, preferences, and network bandwidth availabilities. Recently, severe competition in web content delivery market raises great demand for network intelligence to provide value-added functions on top of the basic content delivery network. This includes anti-virus, encryption and watermarking, data compression, language translation, personalization, . . ., etc.

In 1996, the concept of "active network" is proposed (Tennenhouse and Wetherall 1996; Psounis 1999). The basic idea behind is to implement intelligence in the network gateway and proxy and allow data to be manipulated as it passes through the network. The motive of this proposal is to allow more sophisticated web services to be offered efficiently without increasing the burden of or requiring full collaboration from web servers. Furthermore, the concept also goes from the network packet level to the HTTP application level. (Psounis 1999) gives a good overview on the motivations behind active network and suggests three typical network locations (or nodes) where such computation might occur. They are firewall, web proxy, and mobile gateway. All these share the common feature that data manipulation will happen in these nodes. The authors also predict that with the increasing demand of active network capabilities from applications, new network protocols as well as system architectures will be needed over the traditional passive proxy gateway.

There are two basic approaches to implement active network. They are active packets and active nodes. Active packet approach suggests that packets passing through the network can carry data as well as executable code (Tennenhouse and Wetherall 1996). Execution of the code might be triggered in network nodes when some predefined condition is satisfied. Active node approach requires the network nodes to have the executable code installed inside. When data is passed through an active node, they might be manipulated or transformed by executing the code in the node. Again, the triggering is based on some predefined conditions. Some typical examples for active nodes are firewall and request redirection for load-balancing. With the introduction of intelligence and computation into the network, they find that the scalability and efficiency of web services can be greatly improved. The ultimate goal of active network, as is suggested by the authors, is the definition of a small set of APIs upon which wide range of applications can be programmed (Tennenhouse and Wetherall 1996; Psounis 1999;

Campell et al. 1999).

Initially, intelligence and computation in an active network are suggested to take place in routers and switches. However, with more new applications needed to be migrated into the network, it is found that scalability is a big issue and extension of protocols at that level is not easy (Fry and Ghosh 1999; Ghosh et al. 2001). As a result, researchers and developers turn to proxy server and use it as the basic platform for active network. The result is called "application level active network" or ALAN because it is built at the HTTP application level instead of the network packet level. The core of the ALAN is the dynamic proxy server, or DPS.

A good example to illustrate the benefits and potentials of the ALAN concept is the funnelWeb project from Australia (Fry and Ghosh 1999; Ghosh et al. 2000; Mac Larty and Fry 2000; Ghosh et al. 2001). The active network service in the funnelWeb is provided through a cluster of DPSs. Value-added functions for DPSs are implemented as proxylets which are stored in a proxylet server. They are downloaded from the proxylet server to the DPSs on demand. To support the addition of new network protocols, a dynamic protocol stack is defined in the funnelWeb. The dynamic protocol stack is stored in a dynamic protocol server. Whenever a certain new protocol is needed, the DPSs will download it from the dynamic protocol server and use it to communicate with other servers in the ALAN. Fry and Ghosh (1999) also show how audio streaming and data compression can be achieved through the funnelWeb. Later, researchers of the ALAN (MacLarty and Fry 2000) also give solutions to the caching requirements and to the dynamic web content adaptation to meet the unique requirements of individual clients. Finally, to complete the funnelWeb system architecture as an application level active network, application level routing within the funnelWeb is defined (Ghosh et al. 2000).

Besides the basic content transformation and adaptation, there are other important related research issues that need to be addressed by the ALAN. For example, execution of some value-added function in an ALAN might require interaction with its environment to obtain input parameters to the function (Kornblum et al. 2001). When a network becomes active, an efficient way is also needed to provide dynamic installation of network services and flexibility to the active code (Fernando et al. 2001). Other topics such as QoS and security in active network are also investigated (Marshall and Roadknight 2001; Karnouskos 2001). Another research issue is the definition of a new language to facilitate the programmability of the ALAN (Wakeman et al. 2001).

2.3 Basic Technologies in Active Network

The basic idea of active network is to implement intelligence in the network proxy gateway for real-time content transformation and adaptation. Before we research into active network, it is important to have a deeper understanding of the technologies behind it. The first set of technologies is the basic proxy caching on which all intelligence is built. Since the first application of active network is image transcoding for pervasive Internet access, it is also important to study its related work thoroughly. The last set of technologies is related to real-time content adaptation for quality-based web content delivery. In this set, it will cover web data format, markup language support, system framework and protocols. All these will be discussed in detail in the next few sections.

2.3.1 Basic Proxy Caching

Since the introduction of World Wide Web, user perceived latency is always an important concern to all web applications. Although network bandwidth is kept being improved, it is often offset by the increasing multimedia data size and user's expectation. To address this speed problem, researchers try to apply the idea of caching from the processor memory and parallel processing systems to the web. This results in the popular deployment of web proxy caching on Internet infrastructures (Luotonen and Altis 1994), as it is a proven technology to reduce the HTTP traffic by 30% to 50%.

The concept of a proxy server is first introduced as a mechanism to increase the security protection for clients behind a firewall (Luotonen and Altis 1994). It serves as the gateway for information exchange between the clients behind it and the web servers outside on Internet. Client information can be hidden from the web servers and only the proxy location is made known to the Internet. The first proxy server built is an HTTP proxy, which handles all HTTP requests and replies for web access.

Immediately after the deployment of proxy server, researchers find that there is substantial amount of web data sharing among clients behind the same proxy. This leads to the introduction of caching in proxy, resulting in today's web caching or proxy caching (Luotonen and Altis 1994; Glassman 1994). Since its working principle is still based on the reference localities, the reuse of data in the proxy cache near the clients will improve user perceived latency of web access and reduce the bandwidth consumption of the network and web server. This also changes the original two-tiers client-server structure to the three-tiers client-proxy-server model. Although there is some initial concern about the overhead in the proxy cache in case of a reference miss, it is proven later that the additional delay in the user perceived time is negligible and it is outweighed by the significant benefits gained in proxy cache deployment.

Due to the unique requirements of web access, an efficient proxy cache needs to have fast access, robustness, client transparency, scalability, stability, and load-balancing to deal with the large number of simultaneous heterogeneous user connections. Major research areas in the traditional proxy caching include modeling and prediction of user access pattern (Iyengar et al. 1998; Barford et al. 1999), proxy cache architecture (Wang 1999; Barish and Obraczka 1999; Shi and Karamcheti 2001), replacement policies (Abrams et al. 1995; Cohen and Kaplan 1999), prefetching (Padmanabhan and Mogul 1996; Kroeger et al. 1997; Duchump 1999), cache coherence (Dingle and Partl 1997; Shi and Karamcheti 2001), path routing and resolution (Ross 1997), and performance measurement (Iyengar et al. 1998).

One new area of proxy cache research is the dynamic web caching (Brewington and Cybenko 2000; Lim et al. 2001) and its associated active caching (Loukopoulos et al. 2001). On the web, each object has an attribute, called the freshness of data. It specifies the time period in which the content of the object can be assumed to be fresh or valid without contacting the web server (Wang 1999). To guarantee the freshness of the cached data, HTTP protocol classifies web objects into static objects and dynamic ones. Static objects can be cached in proxy for future reuse while dynamic ones should not be stored in order to avoid data inconsistency with the web server. With the growing popularity of dynamically generated web content (such as those from database), it is generally agreed that current proxy cache performance is bounded by the percentage of dynamic content passing through the proxy (Douglis et al. 1997).

Active caching[1] is a mechanism which researchers propose to address the problem of dynamic web caching. Investigation finds that many web objects such as those related to news and commercial advertisement services change very often. Two major challenges of handling these data are to find out when and how a web object is modified or updated (Douglis et al. 1997; Wills and Mikhailov 1999; Brewington and Cybenko 2000; Lim et al. 2001). In other words, how the cached copy of a web object can be synchronized with its original copy in the web server with minimal effort. Various solutions are proposed. Rowstron et al. (2001), propose a probabilistic model to find out the good time for data synchronization. Zhu and Yang (2001); Flesca et al. (2001) suggest ways to detect the relevant changes in a dynamic web object. Proxy architectures are proposed to cache dynamic web objects; various mechanisms are described to provide efficient synchronization of cached data content with the original copies in the web server (Iyengar and Challenger 1997; Challenger et al. 1998; Holmedahl et al. 1998; Degenaro et al. 2000). Basically, two kinds of data synchronization are mentioned. They are proxy invalidation and server push or announcement for content changes.

An alternative approach to dynamic web caching is to use prefetching to address the user perceived latency problem (Pandey et al. 2001). Instead of keeping a dynamic web object in cache and worrying about its freshness, prefetching chooses to "preload" the object shortly before it is actually requested. In this way, the problem of data freshness can be resolved. Of course, this approach is built on the argument that sequential relationship exists among web object accesses. These prefetching modules in proxy cache are often based on web mining and its association and sequential ruling. Other researchers also suggest the markup language approach (Douglis et al. 1997; Challenger et al. 2000). A markup language such as the HPP can be defined to differentiate the static contents from the dynamic ones in a web page. With this hint, a proxy cache can easily cache the static part and bypass the dynamic one from the cache.

Proxy caching is an essential component in active network where intelligence in content adaptation should be implemented. This is because proxy is the gateway where web data pass through. It is also the place where any reuse of data can be found.

2.3.2 Transcoding for Pervasive Internet Access

With the rapid penetration of the Internet and web into various aspects of people's life, a wide range of devices are being connected to the Internet. Besides the traditional desktop

---

[1] Note that this active caching is different from the active proxy that is studied in the area of active network and adaptive web content delivery network/service.

PCs, handphones, PDAs, and game stations are getting more popular in web browsing (Weiser 1993). Due to the variation of their hardware capabilities (such as computation power, display, and memory) and network connectivity (e.g. modem vs. broadband), web access environment rapidly shifts from homogeneity to heterogeneity. This poses a great challenge to both content and network service providers: how to deliver the best-fit presentation from a single data source to different clients with different requirements and constraints? In this case, the quality of web delivery includes not only the user perceived latency, but also the appropriateness of web presentation and necessity of web data transfer. For example, it is not appropriate to deliver the same quality of an image to a 1,024×768 high-resolution monitor and a black-white WAP based handphone.

The first set of technologies used to address the heterogeneity of clients' need is image transcoding which is defined as the transformation of an image from a higher quality version to a lower quality one (Barrett et al. 1995; Sinclair 1996; Roger 1998; Schechter 2000; IBM 1999). Image transcoding is found to be appropriate in the pervasive Internet access environment because the quality of client display hardware is usually lower and the network connectivity is slower when compared to those in the desktop environment. Furthermore, since the computation power and memory of pervasive devices are usually very limited, transcoding should be done outside the client device hardware. Sinclair (1996) suggests that a more concise communication protocol should be used instead of the normal HTTP and one possible location for transcoding to take place should be the web server. In (WEBSP 2009), a Transcoding Publisher module in IBM's WebSphere is proposed. It is a server-based software that can dynamically translate web content into multiple markup languages and then optimize it for delivery to mobile devices such as PDAs and handphones.

Instead of the web server, researchers find that transcoding should better be taken place in the network proxy. The argument is that a proxy server understands the needs of its clients much better than a web server, and it also allows better scalability and efficiency of the infrastructure. More important, however, is the ability for a proxy cache to synthesize higher quality version of an image from the lower quality version of the image in the local cache together with the additional necessary "delta" content of the image retrieved from the web server (Mogul et al. 1997; Banga et al. 1997). This ends up to be an active network where the intelligence here is the image transcoding to give best-fit presentation of an image to a wide variation of clients with different needs and constraints.

One very good example of proxy-based transcoding system is Pythia and TranSend project from Berkeley (Fox and Brewer 1996). Armando Fox and his team notice that network latency is a big problem for web surfers, especially for those connected through dialup modem. To improve the user perceived latency and bandwidth requirement, they introduce the concept of "distillation", which is defined as a real-time, highly lossy, data-type specific compression technique with preservation of most of the content semantic of a given web object. They also propose another function, called the "refinement", as a complement to the distillation function. While distillation converts an image from an original higher quality version to a lower one, refinement does the reverse, recovering the given image to its original full quality version. With these two techniques, tradeoff between the quality and the download speed of an image can be obtained.

Later, Fox and his team extend the real-time transcoding proxy framework to cover more complex situations in the heterogeneous Internet environment (Fox et al. 1996; Fox et al. 1997a; Fox et al. 1997b; Fox et al. 1998). They point out that with the fast development pace of the Internet and web, it is necessary for the Internet infrastructure to handle all possible kinds of browsing devices that are about to be connected to the net. With a wide variation in their hardware configuration, installed software and network accessing speed, real-time content adaptation is necessary to satisfy the need of these devices. Their solution is still based on the real-time transcoding proxy because of the following reasons. First, transcoding in the network can leverage the existent infrastructure through incremental hardware installation and upgrading. Secondly, the proxy solution can be prototyped rapidly and deployed during the turbulent standardization cycles. Finally, in terms of scalability, proxy solution in the network infrastructure is a more economical solution.

The pioneer work of transcoding proxy by Fox is later expanded into the more general concept of adaptive content delivery in the heterogeneous Internet environment, which we are going to discuss next.

2.3.3 Adaptive Content Delivery

With the success of the transcoding proxy projects for pervasive computing, researchers are convinced with the direction of active proxy with intelligence. The continuous demand for value-added services on the Internet urges researchers to explore technologies for real-time content transformation and adaptation with maximum data reuse in network proxy. This results in the concept of adaptive content delivery (Mohan et al. 1999; Li et al. 1998; Smith et al. 1999; Fox et al. 1996; Fox et al. 1997a; Fox et al. 1997b; Fox et al. 1998; Li et al. 1999b; Chi et al. 2000; Chi et al. 2002; Chi et al. 2004) and drives the basic passive content delivery model to the active content networking paradigm. Under this new direction, there are several main research topics, including data format, markup language, system framework and protocol design. In the next few sections, each of these topics will be surveyed and analyzed thoroughly.

2.3.3.1 Data Format

Data format of an object defines the structure of the content inside and determines how the content can be viewed and manipulated. It is found to be an important factor to determine the efficiency of adaptive web content delivery in at least two different ways: (i) scalability of object retrieval for various levels of quality presentation, and (ii) reusability of partial content of an object to build other quality versions of the same object.

Currently, major data formats found on the Internet are not optimized for adaptive content delivery. For example, multimedia data format such as JPEG and MPEG focuses mainly on better compression ratio, visual effect, and content indexing. Data format for text and html is also defined in terms of content meaning and semantics.

There is no emphasis on features that can assist efficient adaptive web content delivery. Creation of a new presentation from the original multimedia object usually implies a large overhead and this results in the performance problem in real-time transcoding and content adaptation. Data reusability among different presentation versions of an object is also found to be difficult, thus causing significant degradation in cache performance and increasing network bandwidth consumption. Inside a given object such as html, each piece of content actually has its own lifetime (or time to live). However, the granularity of transfer and storage operation as object results in non-cacheability of an entire object even if only a small, localized content change (such as the information of an advertisement banner) is made inside. In the past two years, however, this situation starts to change.

Currently, among all the multimedia objects on the Internet, images can be considered as one of the most popular data types. Since about 50% of the HTTP traffic is due to the image retrieval, content providers are constantly looking for new encoding technologies to reduce image size without sacrificing quality (OPTIMIzing 2000; Taubman et al. 2000; Gormish et al. 2000; Chi et al. 2000; Li et al. 1999a). The result of this effort is the JPEG2000 (JPEG 2K). Due to the properties of wavelet, tiling, progression, and regions of interest, an image of a given quality under JPEG 2000 usually has a substantially smaller size when compared to that under current JPEG.

However, JPEG2000 has a very significant implication to adaptive web content delivery that people often overlook (Skoduas et al. 2001). Due to its wavelet nature, JPEG2000 is a bit-streaming, layered data format, with the basic layer in the front and refinement layers at the end of the object. As a result, the quality of an image presentation under JPEG2000 is directly proportional to the number of first N bytes taken. This makes the real-time transcoding of JPEG2000 practical and easy because it is simply a byte range retrieval with negligible overhead. Reusability of data among various transcoded versions of an image is also possible, as a lower quality version can be used to build a higher quality one by simply retrieving the "delta" difference in the byte range of the image from the web server. This also implies a cumulative effect of image quality when it is deployed in a proxy cache. Given a fixed bandwidth and latency tolerance, the first client user gets a lower quality version of an image while later users can get better ones by combining the lower quality version in the local cache with the additional delta byte range retrieved from the server. Similar observation is also made to the emerging video data formats such as MPEG-4 (Koenen 1999). This shows the potentials of data format to facilitate efficient, adaptive web content delivery.

The concepts of content scalability, progressiveness, and reusability of data format towards adaptive web content delivery can be extended from object level to page level. One good example is the IBM's InfoPyramid (Mohan et al. 1999; Smith et al. 1998). InfoPyramid is a multi-dimensional layered data model used to describe various possible content transformation and adaptation choices in pervasive Internet access. The first dimension is multi-resolution. Given a web object, it can be presented in different resolution versions, with finer ones at the bottom of the "pyramid". The second dimension is multi-modality. A given web object can be of different MIME types. For example, a video clip can be presented as a clip of video, a sequence of static images, or even a text summary. The last dimension is multi-abstraction. The abstraction defines the features and data in the hierarchical order of the data pyramid. For each element object in a given web page, its abstraction has meta-data to describe attributes such as size, resolution, user-preference, . . ., etc. Usually, those with larger size and better quality are at the bottom and those summary ones are at the top of the pyramid.

With the InfoPyramid, a web object can be adapted either horizontally or vertically to meet the client's need while the sem web page to a client, another module associated with the InfoPyramid, called the Customizer, is used to select the best-fit content version of the page objects according to the needs and constraints. Basically, the Customizer turns a web page adaptation into a resource allocation problem. Their result on web server shows that significant reduction in the data transfer and page download time can be obtained. One important design consideration lacking in the InfoPyramid, however, is the data reusability among choices in the infopyramid. This problem becomes more important as the pyramid is getting bigger with more variations from clients hardware, systems, and networks.

In summary, we see that data format can have positive impact on adaptive web content delivery. With proper design and consideration, data format can make real-time content adaptation and delivery feasible and practical. It is also an important determination factor for data reusability among different presentation versions of the same object. More research work is needed to define a universal data model that can facilitate efficient adaptive content delivery and how this data model can map to the current multimedia data formats found on the Internet.

2.3.3.2 Markup Language

Markup language, such as the HTML, is the basic tool to specify the semantics and structure of web information. Traditionally, it describes one single presentation version of a web object, assuming the homogeneity of client's needs and network dynamics. There is no information (or hints) and constructs to describe how the same object/ page should be adapted in case of the heterogeneous pervasive Internet access with wide variation of client's hardware, preferences, and network capabilities. In adaptive web content delivery, such information is essential to allow more appropriate content transformation and adaptation to take place in real-time. This results in the recent extensions to the HTML languages.

The Extensible Markup Language (or XML) is a subset of SGML defined by the W3C (XML 1998; XML 2000) to help pervasive Internet access. Besides its easy implementation, user friendliness, and compatibility to the HTML, one important design goal of the XML is to support adaptive content delivery. For a given well-written, XML-based web page, it is possible to specify different page compositions according to the client's unique constraints and needs. With the hints from the content provider, content adaptation can be done easily and more appropriately.

One good example of such usage is the WML (or Wireless Markup Language)(Cover 2001; WML 2001). It is a markup language based on the XML and is introduced by the mobile communication group. In the wireless world, it is possible to have a wide variation of client hardware and networks. There are also more constraints found in the wireless world than in the wired world. For example, the screen of the browsing device can be very small with low resolution; the computation power of the device is very limited; the wireless network is relatively slower in speed and more expensive (Cover 2001). As a result, besides a common communication protocol interfacing with the basic transportation protocol, a dedicated markup language is needed to facilitate dynamic content adaptation there.

The WML is a "low-cost", XML-based markup language. Compared to the traditional HTML, the WML has unique properties tailored for adaptive content delivery in the wireless world. Information delivered to a WML browser is in the form of "deck of cards". Each card is a standalone piece of information that should be able to be displayed on the relatively smaller screen of mobile devices. By providing more than one card (or deck), a user can select and navigate any section (or different version) of a web site according to his needs and constraints. This approach is to avoid downloading much more information that is not related to him and his browsing device. The WML is widely used today for mobile web access.

Another important markup language for adaptive web content delivery is the Edge Side Includes (or ESI), first proposed by Oracle and Akamai (Nottingham and Liu 2001; ESI 2001). It uses content adaptation in the network, which they call the edge side include, to address the caching problem of dynamic web content. This problem is getting more attention recently because current proxy caching solution has already achieved a reasonable level of performance on the static web content, thus shifting the bottleneck to the non-cacheable dynamic web content. More importantly, the amount of dynamic web content is constantly increasing due to the use of database and other latest web technologies.

The ESI provides a solution to the problem by indicating which part of a web object needs to be generated dynamically (Tsimelzon and Jacobs 2001). Under the ESI, dynamic web content can be cached in an edge server, which is on the distribution side of the Internet. When a web object is retrieved from an edge server, its content will be parsed. The dynamic segments of the object will be retrieved from the original web server while the static segments of the object can be obtained from the cached version. Its operation is actually quite similar to the original SSI (Server Side Include) concept, except that it is now done in the edge server instead. A special invalidation protocol is also defined to ensure the consistency of the dynamic web content cached in the edge server (Jacobs et al. 2001).

Besides the WML and ESI, other markup languages such as the WSDL (Web Service Description Language) (Christensen et al. 2001) are also defined. All these markup languages help the adaptation of web content delivery by providing server (or content provider) hints to the transformation engines. This information is definitely important to content adaptation because content providers are supposed to have good idea on how their content should be transformed. However, more help from the network is also needed because it is often difficult for the static hints to meet the constantly changing requirements from the dynamic pervasive Internet access (e.g. with new browsing devices). Also, collaboration from content providers might sometimes not be available and network providers need to make all the adaptation decisions by themselves.

2.3.3.3 System Frameworks

With the growing demand for pervasive Internet access, a few system frameworks have been proposed to facilitate or model real-time adaptive web content delivery in the past few years. Each of them has its own unique features and all of them aim at solving the heterogeneity of pervasiveness of Internet and web access. In this section, we would like to survey those that are more popular in actual deployment.

The WEBI (or WeB Intermediaries) is an adaptive system framework proposed by IBM to facilitate the development of web-based intermediaries (WEBI 2002; McManus and Nottingham 2001; Hamilton et al. 2001). Observing the continuous migration of server and client applications into the network, researchers in IBM believe that a general framework is needed to simplify and standardize the development of these web intermediaries.

The WEBI is a Java-based system framework designed for such a purpose. Since the web is uni-directional (i.e. only browser initiates transactions) and transactional (i.e. every browser request produces exactly one server response), a WEBI transaction will flow through three basic stages: request editors, generators, and response editors. A request editor receives a request from a client and might modify it before it passes the request to the next level. A generator receives a client request and produces a corresponding response (i.e. a document). A response editor receives a response and might modify the content inside before it passes the response to the next network stage. When all these three steps are completed, the final response will be sent to the client. A fourth type of processing element, the monitor, is designated to receive a copy of the request and response but it does not have any permission to modify the data flow. All these editors, generators, and monitors are referred to as MEGs. For each web transaction, the WEBI dynamically creates a sequence of MEGs to meet some specific requirements. This sequence usually involves elements from the MEG pool of the WEBI. Besides the traditional proxy cache function, the WEBI supports intermediary applications such as content personalization and multimedia data transcoding. Although the WEBI architecture can provide a simple and flexible programming framework for developing web intermediaries (WEBI 2002; McManus and Nottingham 2001; Hamilton et al. 2001), its performance problem limits its practical use to be on the client side instead of in the network proxy.

Another pioneer adaptive system framework is from Berkeley and later Stanford (Fox et al. 1996; Fox et al. 1997a; Fox et al. 1997b; Fox et al. 1998). Armando Fox and his team extend the idea of content transformation in proxy to scalable network devices and propose the "TACC" concept to describe the characteristics of network devices. TACC stands for Transformation, Aggregation, Caching and Customization. They point out that there are three main requirements for network application development. The first one is scalability. If the workload of a network application is increased, the hardware should be able to upgrade its capabilities incrementally to handle the extra workload. The second one is availability. The network application should be a 24x7 service and its hardware and software should have fault tolerant capabilities. The last one is cost effectiveness. Such application needs to be economical to deploy, administer and expand.

The general TACC concept soon becomes the foundation of several adaptive system frameworks that Fox and his team build. With the focus on pervasive computing and data appliance service, they apply the TACC concept to the pervasive Internet access environment and concentrate on the co-operation and services of all kinds of possible pervasive devices inside. This results in their later blueprint for pervasive Internet access (Huang et al. 1999). In this blueprint, there is a centralized structure, called Rome, which acts as the communication center and provides all the necessary adaptation functions for pervasive devices. They argue that in the pervasive environment, a centralized base station and a logically centralized software service center are essential for individual pervasive device to function properly. Based on this Rome concept, an infrastructure-centric adaptive delivery system, called the iRome, is proposed (Fox et al. 2000). To solve the problem of cooperation among client devices, iRome uses three approaches to provide practical solutions. They are web front plus infrastructure proxy (like multibrowsing (Johanson et al. 2001)), pseudo-native code plus infrastructure translator, and PDA native code. One lesson they learnt from all their systems development is that the infrastructure centric solution should be most effectively deployed in proxy server (e.g. ProxiWeb from Berkeley).

In their later work, Fox and his team build another adaptive system, called the "Paths", to investigate the problem of integrating COTS (commercially off the shelf) entities in a ubiquitous computing environment (Kiciman and Fox 2000). They point out that the barrier to COTS in the ubiquitous environment is not simply the different data formats from various pervasive devices. Instead, a truly seamless client experience requires an efficient framework to handle dynamic connection of client's endpoints on demand. "Paths" is such a framework and meditation infrastructure that is extended from the TACC concept. It has three key components: coordinator, mediator, and representative. Each client device is connected to a representative. The mediators are the transformation modules for content. Periodically, the representatives need to announce their presence to the coordinator. Once a request is sent to the Paths system, the coordinator will find a set of suitable mediators to provide the requested service.

Another adaptive system framework worth mentioning here is the CANS (Composable, Adaptive Network Services) project from NYU (Fu et al. 2001). Its framework is mainly made up of three components: drivers, services, and communication adapters. Drivers are standalone mobile code modules, which perform transformation and adaptation on streaming web data. They are similar to the transformation modules in other adaptive delivery networks. In CANS, services are used to export data using standard protocols like the TCP and the HTTP. Communication adapters are used for physical data transmission.

With the CANS, the authors claim that various applications, in particular those legacy ones, can be migrated into the system framework easily and clients with various hardware capabilities and preferences can be served better. They also use the classical example, image transcoding, to show how content adaptation can be done in their framework (Fu et al. 2001; Chang and Karamcheti 2001). They highlight the CANS achievement over other adaptive system delivery frameworks in two aspects. First, they support legacy applications and services. Secondly, they have enabled configuration and distributed adaptation of injected components in response to system conditions.

Another system architecture that the NYU group proposes is the CONCA (or COnsistent Nomadic Content Access) (Shi and Karamcheti 2001). They point out two important trends of web-based content. The first one is the increasing amount of dynamic and personalized content on the web. The second one is the significant growth in "on-the-move" access. Both of these two features need to be considered for any efficient transformation network framework. And the adapted web content needs to be delivered to clients efficiently, independent of their physical location. Furthermore, they also believe that proxy server should be the most appropriate place to build such solution.

However, instead of extending the existing proxy cache structure, the NYU group redesigns a completely new cache structure from scratch to handle dynamic web content, cache transcoded versions of web objects and nomadic nature of users. The design needs cooperation from both the clients and the servers. Clients will give extra information about their preference and device configuration when they send out requests to this adaptive system; servers will decompose web pages into desirable templates. To serve a request, the system tries to select the desirable components for the templates that are generated by the servers. Caching of the templates will be done by their new cache structure. The challenges that this approach is facing, as they point out (Shi and Karamcheti 2001), are efficient mechanisms to obtain document templates, capture user content access profiles in pervasive devices, resource allocation and management, and tradeoff between communication and computation.

All the system frameworks described above contribute to the development of adaptive web content delivery in many different important ways. However, there are two fundamental issues that need further research efforts. The first issue is the real-time performance overhead of triggering the content adaptation. Just like the WEBI, content transformation on the client PC desktop is not an issue of concern for performance. However, if the adaptation is done in a proxy cache with heavy traffic, the mode of transformation, namely streaming vs. buffering, will make a big difference in actual system performance. It is a key factor to determine the practicability of an adaptive system framework.

The second issue is the sharing of data among various transformed versions of the same web object. One of the main advantages of triggering the content adaptation process in proxy cache is the possibility of data reuse. With the growing number of possible pervasive devices and client preferences, the cache hit rate of one transcoded version of an object is expected to be much lower than that of the object (i.e. hit rate of the object, independent of its versions). It is then a big challenge of how one transcoded version of a web object in the local proxy cache can help to reduce the bandwidth requirement and adaptation overhead of forming another transcoded version of the object.

There is no simple answer to these questions because the solution requires support from both the system framework and the multimedia data format. More research efforts are required to make the adaptive system framework both feasible and practicable.

2.3.3.4 Web Protocols

Web protocols are the standards upon which all web applications should be developed. For adaptive web content delivery, there are two types of protocols that need to be taken care of. The first type is the basic HTTP transfer protocol. The second type is the special purpose protocol that is defined for content adaptation. While the first type is quite stable, the second one is still emerging.

Hypertext Transfer Protocol, or HTTP is the basic transport protocol for the web (HTTP0 1996; HTTP1 1999). Besides the basic features for data transport found in HTTP/1.0, the latest version of HTTP, HTTP/1.1, supports a new number of new features that facilitate adaptive web content delivery. The first one is the concept of content negotiation. A web client can specify preference in his request to a web server. The preference can range from the language and text encoding to the quality of the returned images. Based on this information, the server can deliver the appropriate version of the requested web object to the client. To avoid confusion among different versions of the same object, HTTP/1.1 has the VARY header to specify their versions.

Another important feature of HTTP/1.1 for adaptive content delivery is the RANGE request. Traditionally, a web request retrieves the entire full object. However, with the new RANGE request, a web request can specify a certain data range of a web object to be sent to a client. This is what we call the partial object request. The semantic of the RANGE request is so flexible that a client can actually request multiple ranges of data from the same object in one HTTP request. This feature is very important to adaptive content delivery in two ways. With proper support from the layered data format, different quality versions of a web object can be sent to a client with mineral network bandwidth consumption. A proxy cache can also request the refinement layers of a web object using a RANGE request to a web server, combining it with the basic layers of the object in the local proxy cache, and the resulting higher quality object presentation can be sent to the client. Note that this is one effective way to share data among different transocded versions of an object.

For content adaptation protocols, the most representative one is the Internet Content Adaptation Protocol (or I-CAP) (ICAP 2010). The I-CAP is a protocol designed to off-load specific content adaptation functions to dedicated servers, thereby freeing up resources and standardizing the way in which the features are implemented. For example, a server that handles only language translation is inherently more efficient than any standard web server performing many additional tasks.

The I-CAP concentrates on leveraging edge-based devices (proxies and caches) to help deliver value-added services. At the core of this process is the I-CAP client, a cache that will proxy all client transactions and will process them through the I-CAP servers.

These I-CAP servers are focused on a specific function, for example, ad insertion, virus scanning, content translation, language translation, or content filtering. Off-loading value-added services from web servers to the I-CAP servers allows those same web servers to be scaled according to the raw HTTP throughput instead of having to handle these extra tasks. Furthermore, changing functions in the I-CAP-based adaptive content delivery network is easy because only the individual I-CAP servers need to be replaced without affecting the basic system and network architecture.

The I-CAP in its most basic form is a "lightweight" HTTP based remote procedure call protocol. In other words, the I-CAP allows its clients (usually the proxy cache servers) to pass HTTP based (HTML) messages (Content) to the I-CAP servers for adaptation. Adaptation refers to performing the particular value added services (content manipulation) for those associated client requests/responses. The I-CAP is widely accepted by content delivery network companies like Akamai and Network Appliance. One issue of concern, just like any other adaptive content delivery network, is the performance, which is being investigated at this moment. The most recent adaptive content delivery protocol that is being discussed in the IETF is the OPES, which stands for Open Pluggable Edge Services (Taubman et al. 2000; Tomlinson et al. 2001; McHenry et al. 2004). Compared to the I-CAP, it is a more general, flexible, and complete architecture. It defines how network intermediaries or proxies should be extended to deploy services that require transformation on the application data passing through the network. It aims to support multiple protocols so that both existent and future servers can be co-operated together to deliver quality-based content. Just like the I-CAP, the interface between the transformation server and the existing web dataflow is the proxy server. After the proxy server intercepts the application data, it will do either a local or a remote function call to perform the required content transformation or adaptation function on the data.

OPES defines a series of protocols to facilitate the development of such adaptation applications, which they call the proxylets (Maciocco et al. 2001a, 2001b). With these protocols, the proxylets developed by different vendors can be shared among each other. OPES also develops protocols for the markup language that is used by the edge server (Beck and Hofmann 2000; Maciocco and Hofmann 2000; Ng et al. 2001a, 2001b). Together with the protocols for the policy handling (Yang et al. 2001; Rafalow 2000; Beck and Hofmann 2000; Yang and Hofmann 2000; Rafalow et al. 2001), OPES provides a complete system framework for adaptive web content delivery. The framework is very general and flexible, as any new application and application server can be "plugged" into the framework easily as "soft-chips".

Being a newly proposed protocol, OPES is still under development by researchers in the content delivery areas, noticeably driven by industrial companies such as Intel, Cisco, Volera, Lucent, Cacheflow, . . ., etc. No real system supporting OPES is available yet. Another related issue being discussed is the web data integrity. Once the protocol is completely defined, OPES will be a powerful tool not only to facilitate the development of web intermediaries, but also to tamper web content.

Other protocols related to network content transformation and adaptation include the SOAP (Box et al 2000; Nottingham 2001), the WEBI (WEBI 2002; McManus and Nottingham 2001; Hamilton et al. 2001), the WREC (WREC 2000; Cooper et al. 2001), the MIDCOM (MIDCOM 2010; Srisuresh et al. 2001), and the RSERPOOL (RSERPOOL 2001; Tuexen et al. 2001a, 2001b; Loughney et al. 2001; Stewart and Xie 2001; Xie and Stewart 2002). Each of these protocols tries to provide some framework for content transformation and adaptation in the network and has its own unique properties. In fact, some of these protocols, such as the SOAP, lay foundation to the development of the I-CAP and the OPES. However, since they are not as complete as the I-CAP and the OPES, they are not described in detail here. Readers interested in these protocols should refer to their drafts in IETF.

2.4 Adaptive Web Content Delivery Systems Built

During the development and evolution of adaptive web content delivery, several working systems are built and are deployed into real life use. Although most of them are domain specific and not as general as what people want them to be, they actually represent the milestones and maturity of the adaptive web content delivery technologies at that time. In the next few sections, we would like to survey some of the most representative ones.

2.4.1 IBM's Transcoding Proxy

IBM transcoding proxy (Han et al. 1998) is a prototype system to show the potentials of adaptive web content delivery. It is based on the InfoPyramid data model to solve the "best-fit" delivery problem. The main focus of the system is on image transcoding.

For image transcoding, researchers in IBM propose the concept of "image purpose" for web content. In a normal web page, they suggest that the purpose of an embedded image belong to one of these six types: content, decoration, advertisement, information, logo, and navigation [PaS98]. They argue that images used for different purposes should have different quality requirements. Thus, transcoding of a web image can be mapped into two sub-problems. The first one is to identify the purpose of an image. AI techniques and systems are used to automatically identify its purpose and define its required quality. The second one is to use content-based transcoding technique to achieve the required image quality. Since images with lower quality imply smaller size (Chandra and Ellis 1999), reduction of network bandwidth usage is obtained. This is particularly important for large web objects such as image and video (Smith 1999; Smith et al. 1999; Pandey et al. 2001).

In addition to the Customizer module in the web server, IBM researchers also include an Image Transcoding Proxy in the network (Han et al. 1998). This proxy has two unique modules, the policy module and the transformation module. Based on the image purpose, network bandwidth availability and client's characteristics and preference, the policy module will estimate the potential gain of transcoding and will make the decision on the final quality of the transcoded image. Then the transformation module will perform the actual quality conversion of the image. In the system development, the researchers notice that performance in the streaming mode transcoding is very different from that in the "save-and-send" transcoding. To complete the process, a set of Multimedia Content Description Language for the InfoPyramid is also defined. It is mainly based on the XML, which makes it easier to be used by third party users.

2.4.2 Berkeley's Pythia and TranSend

Pythia and TranSend are two transcoding proxy servers that support trading off image quality for download speed. Armando Fox and his team suggest the use of distillation (or transcoding) to help users with slow network access. They argue that with slow network access, users would sacrifice the quality of presentation for download speed. And this tradeoff can be achieved through distillation, a mechanism to convert a high quality image to a lower quality one with smaller size. Pythia is the first distillation HTTP proxy server that they build for this purpose (Fox and Brewer 1996).

Based on Pythia, Fox and his team develop a more advanced transcoding proxy, called the TranSend (Fox et al. 1998; Fox et al. 1997a). TranSend is a transformation proxy that can perform data-type specific distillation and refinement. It has two working principles: (i) it should adapt the content through data-type specific lossy compression, according to the client's variation and preference, and (ii) the transformation should be done on the fly, in a real-time manner. The transformation should be moved away from the clients and servers to the network proxy. Furthermore, the TranSend proxy performs transformation not only on images, but also on Rich Text object such as PS file into plain text object (Fox et al. 1998; Fox et al. 1997a). Another feature of TranSend mentioned by Fox et al. (1996) is the transformation on real-time movie streaming. Generally speaking, it represents a real, practical adaptive content delivery system and is used to serve the dialup Internet users of Berkeley.

2.4.3 Rice's Puppeteer

Puppeteer is an adaptive web content delivery proxy system built by researchers from Rice University (PUPPETEER 2001; Lara et al. 2001). Its target is component-based applications in a mobile environment.

The structure of Puppeteer is a two-proxy pair, each locating on each side of the content delivery network (i.e. one on client side and one on server side). The architecture has four basic modules: kernel, driver, transcoder, and policy. The kernel module is for core communication between the two-proxy pair. It has its own communication language, called the Puppeteer Intermediate Format (or PIF). There are two types of drivers, one for import and the other for export. The import driver does content parsing, structure extraction and format conversion to the PIF. The export driver does the reverse. Transcoders are a set of engines to perform the supported transcoding and transformation functions such as compression. Lastly, the policy is some module like task dispatcher.

The typical workflow in Puppeteer is like this. Upon receiving a web object, the drivers parse it to discover the structure of the data inside. Then transformation is performed on each selected component to give the specific fidelity level it requires.

Finally, the transformed data is exported back to the application.

With the system built for the mobile environment, researchers from Rice show its benefit and practicability. Compared to other adaptive content delivery systems, Puppeteer has one unique design feature. Instead of working on the clients and servers, it focuses on the two-proxy pair that is located on the two edges of the content delivery network. The transparency of this approach to clients and servers is very important because it makes the actual deployment of adaptive web content delivery network much easier.

2.5 Special-Purpose Proxies

Besides the generic adaptive content delivery systems mentioned in the last three sub-sections, there are a few domain-specific systems that are worth mentioning here. Even though their features are very limited, they signify the real impact of adaptive content delivery technologies on web infrastructure and applications.

2.5.1 Compression Proxy

Just like the transcoding proxy for image delivery, automatic text-based data compression is one of the first adaptation applications for quality-based adaptive web content delivery. This application is motivated by the observation that most of the text objects, in particular the HTMLs, are in the uncompressed format. Compression on these text objects can perform in two folds: (i) by reducing the size of the text object, it can be sent to the client faster, (ii) due to the retrieval dependence between the text container object and the embedded objects inside a web page, being able to retrieve the text container object faster accelerates the retrieval of the embedded objects inside. The two representative compression proxies we mention here are from Expanded Networks and Packeteer.

Proxy server products from Expanded Networks (EXPAN 2010) are claimed to have three unique features: selective caching, vertical data analysis, and adaptive packet compression. It is argued that automatic compression on web content should be done selectively and adaptively. For text and HTML objects that are not compressed, automatic web data compression can speed up the process of object downloading. However, for multimedia data objects such as JPEG and MPEG, since they are already in compressed mode, triggering another level of compression only increases the object size and retrieval time. As a result, their compression products only focus on the HTML and text objects in web page retrieval. Together with their vertical data analysis technology, they claim that about 5% to 10% of the network traffic can be saved.

Compression solution from Packeteer is more sophisticated than that from Expanded Networks. They have a series of content delivery products, with features ranging from traffic shaping, and dynamic caching, . . ., etc. to content aware compression, browser based transformation, and speed based transformation. The Content Aware Compression proxy from Packeteer actually functions similar to the Expanded Network's adaptive packet compression. However, their claims and emphases are different. While Expanded Network focuses on reduction in network bandwidth consumption, Packeteer emphasizes on the download time of a web page, where text-based compression can reduce not only the size of the page container object but also the latency dependence gap for the embedded objects inside. The Browser Based Transformation and Speed Based Transformation products are quite similar to the image transcoding systems mentioned previously.

2.5.2 WAP Gateway

Wireless Application Protocol (or WAP) gateway is the network server designed to solve the Internet browsing problems faced by wireless devices. While most slim wireless devices support the WML, the majority of web pages found on the Internet are written in the HTML. Bridging the WML and the HTML worlds in the real-time manner is the challenge that the WAP gateway wants to address.

The two commercial solutions mentioned here are from MobiWay and Atinav (MOBWA 2010; ATINA 2010). The translation WAP gateway from MobiWay (MOBWA 2010) is built on Java. Its main features include the on-demand gathering of the HTTP resource and the "content-based semi-automatic mediator" which translate the HTML to the WML automatically. Atinav's aveAccess WAP gateway is a more sophisticated solution over the MobiWay's ones. It not only translates the HTML pages and emails into the WML format, but also supports VB and Javascripts. These solutions show the importance of adaptive web content delivery when heterogeneous environments using different network layer protocols need to communicate with each other at the application level.

2.5.3 Single Point Transform Server, ASP

Application server provider, or ASP, is one hot technology for the deployment of Internet applications (ASP 2010). It is being used by some adaptive content delivery networks to provide value-added services. EWGate is such a company that provides automatic language translation on the Internet. Users can translate web pages into their preferred languages by passing the requested web pages through the EWGate's ASP servers on the Internet. The semantic and integrity of the web data, such as links and embedded objects are well taken care of in the translation process. Such approach is quite attractive. Its main problem, however, is the performance. Re-routing web content through the ASP introduces unnecessary web page retrieval delay. The centralized ASP is also likely to be one of the performance bottlenecks because such content transformation process is time and resource consuming. More importantly, there is often no efficient caching system in the ASP server to reuse both transformed and original data, thus enhancing the problem of the system and network performance.

2.5.4 Blocking and Filtering

One special application of adaptive web content delivery is content blocking and filtering, which has already become an essential feature for the deployment of many forward proxy networks. Basically, content blocking and filtering can be divided into three types: URL-based, policy-based, and content-based. URL-based blocking works according to a long list of blocked URLs that are classified into different categories. Policy-based blocking is usually implemented with regulations and rules about the access rights of users and retrieval permission of objects according to the object's characteristics such as data type. In both cases, they are implemented in the access control checking of web intermediaries and proxies. Content-based blocking is based on the real-time understanding of the web content passing through the proxy, together with rules for blocking decision. It is also one of the first and most classic examples for adaptive web content delivery.

2.6 Analysis of Existing Adaptive Content Delivery Frameworks and Systems

In the last few sections, a number of adaptive content delivery frameworks and systems are surveyed. Despite their difference in design and applications, they share some common features which serve as the lessons and directions for future adaptive content delivery research.

On the positive side, most of them adapt web object content to lower quality for faster downloading and/or better-fit presentation to the client's hardware. The initial set of successfully deployed applications includes image transcoding, content blocking, and perhaps (partially) data compression. The basic unit of operation and performance measurement is web object. And it is generally agreed that the most suitable place for the adaptation to occur is the proxy server. Several adaptive content delivery frameworks are also proposed. All these lay the foundation on which future adaptive web content delivery research can be built.

There are a number of open issues that require further research and are the determining factors to the success of adaptive content delivery network deployment.

The first issue is about performance. Since what a client requests is a page which consists of one container object and multiple embedded objects, the performance measurement is much more complicated than what most object-based, proxy trace-driven simulation can provide. This is because page retrieval for a client request is actually made up of parallel fetching of objects. With the nature of web dataflow, retrieval dependence among streaming data chunks of the container object and the embedded object requests also makes the performance more difficult to understand. Persistent connection adds another level of complication. Even the primary performance measurement, whether it should be the object retrieval time, page retrieval time, or user perceived time, is still subject for debate.

The second issue is about caching and data reuse. Proxy caching has generally been accepted to be an essential feature of the web infrastructure to reduce bandwidth consumption and offload server workload. If content adaptation is going to take place in proxy, it should not disable the caching function. There are two approaches of handling the caching problem in transformation proxy, to cache the original copy or to cache the transformed copy. Each has its advantages and disadvantages. Having the original version cached, proxy can reduce the traffic between the web server and itself while it can not reuse the transform engine and transform decision. Having the transformed version cached, proxy can reuse the transform engine and transform decision, but it also has more headaches for handling the consistency, validation and ownership problems of the cached data.

The third issue is about transformation process. Although quite a number of adaptive content delivery frameworks and systems are proposed, very little description is given on how and when the transformation should occur and its impact on the overall system performance. Since the proxy makes the content delivery network to be a three-tiers architecture, detailed understanding on what, when, and how sub-tasks of a typical adaptation function should occur in which phase of this three-tiers architecture is necessary to build a more complete, general framework for adaptive content delivery. Due to the streaming nature of web data, content buffering in the proxy is also another important topic of study.

The last issue is about the scope of studying adaptive content delivery network. Most of the previous work focuses on the system architecture and the supported functionality of the network. However, as we point out earlier, data format and protocol play an important role in determining their feasibility and practicability. It is worthwhile to integrate them into the study and design of adaptive content delivery network.

2.7 Summary

In this chapter, we survey the evolution of active network concept and give examples on frameworks and systems that are developed in each evolution stage. At the very beginning, active network is just a concept. Later, with the growth of pervasive computing, adaptive content delivery systems, mainly in the form of transcoding proxies, start to appear. The rapid demand of the adaptive content delivery network services results in the research in protocols, generalized system frameworks and their APIs to the applications, languages support, and data format. We also point out some of the open issues for research. These include performance definition and study, caching and reuse of transformed data, detail study of the workflow in the transformation process, and the interaction of content transformation and adaptation with data formats and protocols.

References

(Abrams et al. 1995) Abrams M, Standridge C R, Abdulla G et al (1995) Caching Proxies: Limitations and Potentials. In: Proceedings of the 4th International WWW Conference, Boston, Massachusetts, USA, December 1995

(ASP 2010) ASPnews.com. http://www.aspnews.com. Accessed 15 April 2010

(ATINA 2010) Atinav Inc-aveAccess WAP Gateway. http://www.atinav.com. Accessed 15 April 2010

(Barford et al. 1999) Barford P, Bestavros A, Bradley A et al (1999) Changes in Web client access patterns: Characteristics and caching implications. World Wide Web 2(1): 15-28

(Banga et al. 1997) Banga G, Douglis F, Rabinovich M (1997) Optimistic Deltas for WWW Latency Reduction. In: Proceedings of the 1997 USENIX Annual Technical Conference, Anaheim, California, USA, January 1997

(Barrett et al. 1997) Barrett R, Maglio PP, Kellem DC (1997) How to Personalize the Web. In: Proceedings of ACM SIGCHI 97, Hyatt Regency Atlanta Hotel, Atlanta, Georgia, USA, March 22-27, 1997

(Barish and Obraczka 1999) Barish G, Obraczka K (1999) A Survey of World Wide Web Caching. http://citeseer.ist.psu.edu/cache/papers/cs/10228/ftp: zSzzSzftp.usc.eduzSzpubzSzcsinfozSztech-reportsz SzpaperszSz99-713.ps.gz/ barish99survey.ps.gz. Accessed 14 April 2010

(Beck and Hofmann 2003) Beck A, Hofmann M (2003) IRML: A Rule Specification Language for Intermediary Services. http://tools.ietf.org/id/draft-beck-opes-irml. Accessed 14 April 2010

(Box et al. 2000) Box D, Ehnebuske D, Kakivaya G et al (2000) Simple Object Access Protocol (SOAP) 1.1, W3C Note 08. http://www.w3.org/TR/SOAP. Accessed 14 April 2010

(Brewington and Cybenko 2000) Brewington BE, Cybenko G (2000) How dynamic is the web? In: Proceedings of WWW9, Amsterdam, the Netherlands, May 15-19, 2000

(Campell et al. 1999) Campell AT, De Meer H, Kounavis ME et al (1999) A Survey of Programmable Networks. ACM Computer Communications Review 29 (2): 7-24

(Christensen et al. 2001) Christensen E, Curbera F Meredith G et al (2001) Web Service Definition Language (WSDL). http://www.w3.org/TR/wsdl. Accessed 14 April 2010

(Chandra and Ellis 1999) Chandra S, Ellis CS (1999) JPEG Compression Metric as a Quality Aware Image Transcoding. In: Proceedings of 2nd USENIX Symposium on Internet Technologies and Systems, Boulder, Colorado, USA, October 11-14, 1999

(Challenger et al. 2000) Challenger J, Iyengar A, Witting K et al (2000) A Publishing System for Efficiently Creating Dynamic Web Content. In: Proceedings of INFOCOM, Tel Aviv, Israel, 2000

(Challenger et al. 1998) Challenger J, Iyengar A, Dantzig P (1998) A Scalable and Highly Available System for Serving Dynamic Data at Frequently Accessed Web Sites. In: Proceedings of ACM/IEEE Supercomputing '98, Orlando, Florida, USA, November 1998

(Chang and Karamcheti 2001) Chang F, Karamcheti V (2001) A Framework for Automatic Adaptation of Tunable Distributed Applications. Cluster Computing: Journal of Networks, Software and Applications 4(1): 49-62

(Chi et al. 2004) Chi CH, Li X, Wang HG (2004) Accelerating Web Page Retrieval Through Object Usage Declaration. In: Proceedings of the 37th Annual Simulation

Symposium, Arlington, VA, USA, 2004
(Chi et al. 2002) Chi CH, Li X, Lam KY (2002) Understanding the Object Retrieval Dependence of Web Page Access In: Proceedings of the 10th IEEE/ACM International Symposium on Modeling, Analysis and Simulation of Computer and Telecommunication Systems, Fort Worth, USA, October 2002
(Chi et al. 2000) Chi CH, Li X, Lim A (2000) Dynamically Transcoding Data Quality for Faster Web Access. In: Proceedings of the 8th International Conference on High Performance Computing and Networking Europe, Amsterdam, Netherland, May 2000. Lecture Notes in Computer Science, vol 1823. Springer, p527
(Cohen and Kaplan 1999) Cohen E, Kaplan H (1999) Exploiting Regularities in Web Traffic Patterns for Cache Replacement. In: Proceedings of the Annual ACM Symposium on Theory of Computing, Atlanta, Georgia, USA, May 1999
(Cooper et al. 2001) Cooper I, Melve I, Tomlinson G (2001) Internet Web Replication and Caching Taxonomy. In: IETF Internet drafts. http://www.rfc-editor.org/rfc/rfc3040.txt. Accessed 14 April 2010
(Cover 2001) Cover R (2001) WAP Wireless Markup Language Specification (WML). http://www.oasis-open.org/cover/wap-wml.html. Accessed 14 April 2010
(Degenaro et al. 2000) Degenaro L, Iyengar A, Lipkind I et al (2000) A Middleware System Which Intelligently Caches Query Results. In: Proceedings of IFIP/ACM Middleware Conference, New York, NY, USA, April 4-8, 2000
(Dingle and Partl 1997) Dingle A, Partl T (1997) Web Cache Coherence. In: Proceedings of 5th International World Wide Web Conference, Santa Clara, CA, USA, May 1997
(Douglis et al. 1997) Douglis F, Haro A, Rabinovich M (1997) HPP: HTML Macro-Preprocessing to Support Dynamic Document Caching. In: Proceedings of USENIX Symposium on Internet Technologies and Systems, Monterey, CA, USA, December 1997
(ESI 2001) ESI-Accelerating E-Business Applications (2001) http://www.edge-delivery.org. Accessed 14 April 2010
(EXPAN 2010) Expand Networks (2010) http://www.expand.com. Accessed 14 April 2010
(Fernando et al. 2001) Fernando A, Williams D, Fekete A et al (2001) Dynamic network service installation in an active network. Computer Networks 36 (1): 35-48
(Flesca et al. 2001) Flesca S, Furfaro F, Masciari E (2001) Monitoring Web Information Changes. In: Proceedings of ITCC, Las Vegas, NV, USA, 2001
(Fox and Brewer 1996) Fox A, Brewer EA (1996) Reducing WWW Latency and Bandwidth Requirements via Real-Time Distillation. In: Proceedings of the 5th International World Wide Web Conference (WWW-5), Paris, France, May 1996
(Fox et al. 1996a) Fox A, Gribble SD, Brewer EA et al (1996) Adapting to Network and Client Variability via On-Demand Dynamic Distillation. In: Proceedings of the 7th International Conference on Architectural Support for Programming Languages and Operating Systems (ASPLOS-VII), Cambridge, MA, USA, October 1996
(Fox et al. 1997a) Fox A, Gribble SD, Chawathe Y et al (1997) Cluster-Based

Scalable Network Services. In: Proceedings of the 16th International Symposium on Operation Systems Principles (SOSP-16), St. Malo, France, October 1997

(Fox et al. 1997b) Fox A, Gribble SD, Chawathe Y et al (1997) Orthogonal Extensions to the WWW User Interface Using Client-Side Technologies. In: Proceedings of the 10th Annual Symposium on User Interface Software and Technology (UIT 97), Banff, Canada, October 1997

(Fox et al. 1998) Fox A, Gribble SD, Chawathe Y et al (1998) Adapting to Network and Client Variation Using Active Proxies: Lessons and perspectives. IEEE Personal Communications 5: 10-19

(Fox et al. 2000) Fox A, Johanson B, Hanrahan P et al (2000) Integrating Information Appliances into an Interactive Workspace. IEEE Computer Graphics & Applications 20(2): 54-65

(Fry and Ghosh 1999) Fry M, Ghosh A (1999) Application level active networking. Computer Networks 31 (7): 655-667

(Fu et al. 2001) Fu X, Shi W, Akkerman A et al (2001) CANS: Composable, Adaptive Network Services Infrastructure. In: Proceedings of USENIX Symposium on Internet Technologies and Systems (USITS), San Francisco, California, USA, March 2001

(Ghosh et al. 2001) Ghosh A, Fry M, MacLarty G (2001) An Infrastructure for Application Level Active Networking. Computer Networks 36(1): 5-20

(Ghosh et al. 2000) Ghosh A, Fry M, Crowcroft J (2000) An Architecture for Application Layer Routing. In: Proceedings of IWAN, Tokyo, Japan, October 16-18, 2000

(Glassman 1994) Glassman S (1994) A Caching Relay for the World-Wide Web. In: Proceedings of 1st International World-Wide Web Conference, CERN, Geneva, Switzerland, May 1994

(Gormish et al. 2000) Gormish MJ, Lee D, Marcellin MW (2000) JPEG-2000: Overview, Architecture and Applications. In: Proceedings of ICIP '2000, Vancouver, Canada, 2000

(Han et al. 1998) Han R, Bhagwat P, LaMaire R et al (1998) Dynamic Adaptation In an Image Transcoding Proxy For Mobile Web Browsing. IEEE Personal Communications 2: 8-17

(Hamilton et al. 2001) Hamilton M, Cooper I, Li D (2001) Requirements for a Resource Update Protocol. In: IETF Internet drafts. http://tools.ietf.org/html/draft-ietf-webi-rup-reqs-00. Accessed 14 April 2010

(Holmedahl et al. 1998) Holmedahl V, Smith B, Yang T (1998) Cooperative Caching of Dynamic Content on a Distributed Web Server. In: Proceedings of 7th IEEE International Symposium on High Performance Distributed Computing, Chicago, IL, USA, 1998

(Huang et al. 1999) Huang AC, Ling BC, Ponnekanti S et al (1999) Pervasive Computing: What is it good for? In: Proceedings of the Workshop on Mobile Data Management (MobiDE) in conjunction with ACM MobiCom '99, Seattle, WA, USA, September 1999

(IBM 1999) White Paper (1999) IBM Transcoding Solution and Services. http://www.research.ibm.com/networked_data_systems/transcoding/transcodef.pdf. Accessed 14 April 2010

(ICAP 2010a) ICAP-Forum (2010) Internet Content Adaptation Protocol (I-CAP). http://www.icap-forum.org. Accessed 14 April 2010

(Iyengar and Chanllenger 1997) Iyengar A, Challenger J (1997) Improving Web Server Performance by Caching Dynamic Data. In: Proceedings of USENIX Symposium on Internet Technologies and Systems, Monterey, California, USA, 1997

(Iyengar et al. 1998) Iyengar AK, MacNair EA, Squillante MS et al (1998) A General Methodology for Characterizing Access Patterns and Analyzing Web Server Performance. In: Proceedings of the International Symposium on Modeling, Analysis and Simulation of Computer and Telecommunication Systems (MASCOTS'98), Montreal, Canada, July 1998

(Jacobs et al. 2001) Jacobs L, Ling G, Liu X (2001) ESI Invalidation Protocol. In W3C Note 04. http://www.w3.org/TR/esi-invp. Accessed 14 April 2010

(Johanson et al. 2001) Johanson B, Ponnekanti SR, Sengupta C et al (2001) Multibrowsing: Moving Web Content across Multiple Displays. In: Technical Note, UBICOMP 2001, Atlanta, Geogia, USA, September 2001

(JPEG 2000) "JPEG 2000 image coding system", JPEG 2000 Final committee draft version 1.0, (ISO/IEC 15444-1), August 2000

(Karnouskos 2001) Karnouskos S (2001) Security implications of implementing active network infrastructures using agent technology. Computer Networks 36 (1): 87-100

(Kiciman and Fox 2000) Kiciman E, Fox A (2000) Using Dynamic Mediation to Integrate COTS Entities in a Ubiquitous Computing Environment. In: Proceedings of the 2nd International Symposium on Handheld and Ubiquitous Computing (HUC2k) Bristol, England, September 2000. Lecture Notes in Computer Science, vol 1927. Springer, p 211

(Koenen 1999) Koenen R (1999) MPEG-4: Multimedia for our time. IEEE Spectrum, 36(2): 26-33

(Kornblum et al. 2001) Kornblum JA, Raz D, Shavitt Y (2001) The active process interaction with its environment. Computer Networks 36 (1): 21-34

(Kroeger et al. 1997) Kroeger TM, Long DE, Mogul JC (1997) Exploring the Bounds of Web Latency Reduction from Caching and Prefetching. In: Proceedings of USENIX Symposium on Internet Technologies and Systems, Monterey, California, USA, December 1997

(Lara et al. 2001) Lara Ede, Wallach DS, Zwaenepoel W (2001) Puppeteer: Component-based Adaptation for Mobile Computing. In: Proceedings of the 3rd Usenix Symposium on Internet Technologies and Systems, San Francisco, California, USA, March 2001

(Li et al. 1999a) Li X, Chi CH, Deng J et al (1999) Layered Model for Web Multimedia Data and its Implications to Bandwidth Load-Balancing. In: Proceedings of the 3rd World Multiconference on Systemics, Cybernetics, and Informatics, Orlando, FL, USA, August 1999

(Li et al. 1999b) Li X, Chi CH, Dong CL et al (1999) Active Information Transformation Framework for Web Proxy. In: Proceedings of the 3rd World Multiconference on Systemics, Cybernetics, and Informatics, Orlando, FL, USA, August 1999

(Li et al. 1998) Li CS, Mohan R, Smith JR (1998) Multimedia Content Description in the InfoPyramid. In: IEEE Proceedings of Int. Conf. Acoust. Speech, Signal Processing (ICASSP), Special session on Signal Processing in Modern Multimedia Standards, Seattle, WA, USA, May 1998

(Lim et al. 2001) Lim L, Wang M, Padmanabhan S et al (2001) Characterizing Web Document Change. In: Proceedings of the 2nd International Conference on Web-Age Information Management (WAIM '01), Xi'an, China, July 9-11, 2001

(Loukopoulos et al. 2001) Loukopoulos T, Kalnis P, Ahmad I et al (2001) Active Caching of On-Line-Analytical-Processing Queries in WWW Proxies. In: Proceedings of the International Conference on Parallel Processing, Valencia, Spain, September 2001

(Loughney et al. 2001) Loughney J, Stillman M, Tuexen M et al (2001) Comparison of Protocols for Reliable Server Pooling. In: IETF Internet drafts. http://ftp.roedu.net/mirrors/ftp.ietf.org/internet-drafts/draft-ietf-rserpool-comp-11.txt. Accessed 14 April 2010

(Luotonen and Altis 1994) Luotonen A, Altis K (1994) World Wide Web proxies. Computer Networks and ISDN Systems 27(2): 147-154

(MacLarty and Fry 2000) MacLarty G, Fry M (2000) Policy-based Content Delivery: An Active Network Approach. In: Proceedings of WCW'00, Lisbon, Portugal, 2000

(Marshall and Roadknight 2001) Marshall IW, Roadknight C (2001) Provision of quality of service for active services. Computer Networks 36 (1): 75-85

(Maciocco et al. 2001a) Maciocco C, Yang L, Condry M (2001) Protocols characteristics for Proxylets & Rule downloading. In: OPES Workshop, New York, USA, February 2001

(Maciocco et al. 2001b) Maciocco C, Yang L, Condry M (2001) Proxylet, Meta-data, naming, generic issues. In: OPES Workshop, New York, USA, February 2001

(McHenry et al. 2004) McHenry S, Babir A, Burger E et al (2004) RFC3752: Open Pluggable Edge Services (OPES) Use Cases and Deployment Scenarios, 2004

(McManus and Nottingham 2001) McManus P, Nottingham M (2001) Requirements for Intermediary Discovery and Description. In: IETF Internet drafts. http://tools.ietf.org/html/draft-ietf-webi-idd-reqs. Accessed 14 April 2010

(MIDCOM 2010) Middlebox Communication (midcom) Charter. http://www.ietf.org/html.charters/midcom-charter.html. Accessed 14 April 2010

(MOBWA 2010) Mobileways. de-home for fine mobile applications. http://mobileways.de. Accessed 14 April 2010

(Mogul et al. 1997) Mogul JC, Douglis F, Feldmann A et al (1997) Potential benefits of delta-encoding and data compression for HTTP. In: Proceedings of the ACM SIGCOMM'97, Cannes, French Riviera, France, September 1997

(Maciocco and Hofmann 2000) Maciocco C, Hofmann M (2000) OMML: OPES Meta-data Markup Language. In: IETF Internet drafts. http://xml.coverpages.org/draft-maciocco-opes-omml-00.txt. Accessed 14 April 2010

(Mohan et al. 1999) Mohan R, Smith JR, Li CS (1999) Adapting Multimedia Internet Content For Universal Access. IEEE Transactions on Multimedia, March 1999: 104-114

(Ng et al. 2001a) Ng CW, Tan PY, Cheng H (2001) Sub-System Extension to IRML. In: IETF Drafts. http://tools.ietf.org/html/draft-ng-opes-irmlsubsys-00. Accessed 14 April 2010

(Ng et al. 2001b) Ng CW, Tan PY, Cheng H (2001) Quality of Service Extension to IRML. In: IETF Drafts. http://tools.ietf.org/html/draft-ng-opes-irmlqos-00. Accessed 14 April 2010

(Nottingham and Liu 2001) Nottingham M, Liu X (2001) Edge Architecture Specification. In: W3C Note 04. http://www.w3.org/TR/edge-arch. Accessed 14 April 2010

(Nottingham 2001) Nottingham M (2001) SOAP Optimisation Modules: Response Caching. In: W3C Archives. http://lists.w3.org/Archives/Public/www-ws/2001Aug/att-0000/ResponseCache.html. Accessed 14 April 2010

(OPTIMIZING 2000) Optimizing Web Graphics: Compression. In: WebRef. http://www.webreference.com/dev/graphics/compress.html. Accessed 14 April 2010

(Padmanabhan and Mogul 1996) Padmanabhan V N, Mogul J C (1996) Using Predictive Prefetching to Improve World Wide Web Latency. ACM SIGCOMM Computer Communication Review 26(3): 22-36

(Pandey et al. 2001) Pandey A, Srivastava J, Shekhar S (2001) A Web Proxy Server with an Intelligent Prefetcher for Dynamic Pages Using Association Rules. In: Proceedings of SIAM Workshop on Web Mining, Chicago, IL, USA, 2001

(PICS 2009) Platform for Internet Content Selection (PICS). In: W3C. http://www.w3.org/PICS. Accessed 14 April 2010

(Psounis 1999) Psounis K (1999) Active Networks: Applications, Security, Safety, and Architectures. IEEE Communications Surveys 2(1): 2-16

(PUPPETEER 2001) Puppeteer. http://www.cs.rice.edu/CS/Systems/Puppeteer/index.html. Accessed 14 April 2010

(Rafalow 2000) Rafalow L (2000) Open Pluggable Edge Services. In: IETF. http://www.ietf.org/proceedings/53/120.htm. Accessed 14 April 2010

(Rafalow et al. 2001) Rafalow L, Yang L, Beck A (2001) Policy Requirements for Edge Services. In: IETF. http://tools.ietf.org/id/draft-rafalow-opes-policy-requirements-00.txt. Accessed 14 April 2010

(Roger 1998) Roger D (1998) The convenience of small devices. In: IBM Think Research No.3. http://domino.research.ibm.com/comm/wwwr_thinkresearch.nsf/pages/bergman398.html. Accessed 14 April 2010

(Rowstron et al. 2001) Rowstron AIT, Lawrence N, Bishop CM (2001) Probabilistic modelling of replica divergence. In: Proceedings of HotOS VIII, Schoss Elmau, Germany, May 2001

(Ross 1997) Ross K (1997) Hash Routing for Collections of Shared Web Caches. IEEE Network 11(6): 37-44

(RSERPOOL 2001) Reliable Server Pooling (rserpool) Charter. (2001) In: IETF Internet drafts. http://www.ietf.org/html.charters/rserpool-charter.html. Accessed 14 April 2010

(Schechter 2000) Schechter B (2000) Seeing the light: IBM's vision of life beyond the PC. In: IBM research No. 2, 2000. http://domino.research.ibm.com/comm/wwwr_thinkresearch.nsf/pages/pervasive199.html. Accessed 14 April 2010

(Shi and Karamcheti 2001) Shi W, Karamcheti V (2001) CONCA: An Architecture for Consistent Nomadic Content Access. In: Proceedings of Workshop on Caching, Coherence, and Consistency (W3C), International Conference of Supercomputing, Hamburg, Germany, June 2001

(Sinclair 1996) Sinclair M (1996) Mobile Computing on the Move. In: IBM research No.3, 1996. http://domino.research.ibm.com/comm/wwwr_thinkresearch.nsf/pages/mobile396.html. Accessed 14 April 2010

(Skoduas et al. 2001) Skoduas A, Christopoulos C, Ebrahim T (2001) The JPEG 2000 still image compression standard. IEEE SP Magazine, vol. 18, Sep. 2001: 36-58

(Smith et al. 1999) Smith JR, Castelli V, Li CS (1999) Adaptive Storage, Retrieval of Large Compressed Images. In: Proceedings of IS&T/SPIE Symposium on Electronic Imaging: Science Technology-Storage & Retrieval for Image, Video Database VII, San Jose, CA, January 1999

(Smith 1999) Smith JR (1999) VideoZoom Spatio-temporal video browser. IEEE Trans. Multimedia 1(2): 157-171

(Smith et al. 1998b) Smith JR, Mohan R, Li CS (1998) Transcoding Internet Content for Heterogenous Client Devices. In: Proceedings of IEEE International Symposium On Circuits, Syst. (ISCAS), Special session on Next Generation Internet, Monterey, CA, USA June 1998

(Srisuresh et al. 2001) Srisuresh P, Kuthan J, Rosenberg J et al (2001) Middlebox Communication Architecture and framework. In IETF Internet drafts. http://www.rfc-editor.org/rfc/rfc3303.txt. Accessed 14 April 2010

(Stwart and Xie 2002) Stewart S, Xie Q (2002) Aggregate Server Access Protocol (ASAP) . In: IETF Internet drafts. http://tools.ietf.org/html/rfc5352. Accessed 14 April 2010

(Taubman et al. 2000) Taubman D, Ordenlich E, Weinberger M et al (2000) Embedded Block Coding in JPEG 2000. In: Proceedings of ICIP'2000, Vancouver, Canada, 2000

(Tennenhouse and Wetherall 1996) Tennenhouse D, Wetherall D (1996) Towards an Active Network Architecture. Computer Communication Review 26(2), April 1996: 81-94

(Tomlinson et al. 2001) Tomlinson G, Chen R, Hofmann M (2001) A Model for Open Pluggable Edge Services. In: IETF 51. http://tools.ietf.org/html/draft-tomlinson-opes-model-00.Accessed 14 April 2010

(Tsimelzon and Jacobs 2001) Tsimelzon M, Jacobs L (2001) ESI Language

Specification 1.0. In: W3C Note 04. http://www.w3.org/TR/esi-lang. Accessed 14 April 2010

(Tuexen et al. 2001a) Tuexen M, Xie Q, Stewart R et al (2001) Requirements for Reliable Server Pooling. In: IETF Internet drafts. http://www.ietf.org/rfc/rfc3237.txt. Accessed 14 April 2010

(Tuexen et al. 2001b) Tuexen M, Xie Q, Stewart R et al (2001) Architecture for Reliable Server Pooling. In: IETF Internet drafts. http://64.170.98.42/html/draft-ietf-rserpool-arch-12. Accessed 14 April 2010

(Wakeman et al. 2001) Wakeman I, Jeffrey A, Owen T et al (2001) SafetyNet: A language-based approach to programmable networks. Computer Networks 36 (1): 101-114

(Wang 1999) Wang J (1999) A Survey of Web Caching Schemes for the Internet. In: Proceedings of ACM SIGCOMM'99, Cambridge, Massachusetts, USA

(WEBI 2002) Web Intermediaries (webi) Charter. In: IETF Internet drafts. http://datatracker.ietf.org/wg/webi/charter. Accessed 14 April 2010

(WEBSP 2009) Web Sphere: Transcoding publisher. http://www-01.ibm.com/software/pervasive/transcoding_publisher. Accessed 14 April 2010

(Weiser 1993) Weiser M (1993) Some Computer Science Problems in Ubiquitous Computing. Communications of the ACM, July 1993: 75-83

(Wilson 1999) Wilson, T (1999) E-biz bucks lost under ssl strain. In: Internet Week Online, May 20, 1999, http://archives.neohapsis.com/archives/isn/1999-q2/0039.html. Accessed 14 April 2010

(Wills and Mikhailov 1999) Wills CE, Mikhailov M (1999) Towards a Better Understanding of Web Resources and Server Responses for Improved Caching. In: Proceedings of WWW8, Toronto, Canada, May 1999

(WML 2001) Wireless Markup Language 2.0 (2001) http://www.openmobilealliance.org/tech/affiliates/wap/wap-238-wml-20010911-a.pdf. Accessed 14 April 2010

(WREC 2000) Web Replication and Caching (wrec). (2000) In: IETF Internet drafts. http://datatracker.ietf.org/wg/wrec/charter. Accessed 14 April 2010

(Xie and Stewart 2002) Xie Q, Stewart R (2002) Endpoint Name Resolution Protocol. In: IETF Internet drafts. http://www.ietf.org/proceedings/53/slides/rserpool-3/index.html. Accessed 14 April 2010

(XML 1998) Extensible Markup Language (XML) 1.0. (1998) In: W3C. http://www.w3.org/TR/1998/REC-xml-19980210. Accessed 14 April 2010

(XML 2000) Extensible Markup Language (XML) 1.0 (Second Edition) (2000) In: W3C. http://www.w3.org/TR/2000/REC-xml-20001006. Accessed 14 April 2010

(Yang et al. 2001) Yang L, Maciocco C, Condry M (2001) Rule Processing and Service Execution. In: OPES Workshop, New York, USA, February 2001

(Zhu and Yang 2001) Zhu HC, Yang T (2001) Class-based Cache Management for Dynamic Web Content. In: Proceedings of INFOCOM, Anchorage, Alaska, USA, 2001

3

Chunk-Level Performance Study for Web Page Latency

3.1 Introduction

In adaptive web content delivery, two main areas of research are the "world-wide-wait" (or user's retrieval latency) problem and the value-added intermediary services provided in active network (ICAP 2010a; OPES 2001). Sometimes, intermediary services are also related to the latency problem because they perform content optimization (such as compression) for faster content delivery.

User's retrieval latency for web page is always a big concern to most Internet content and service providers. The argument here is that the bandwidth demand and the client's expectation on service increase much faster than what the upgrading of network bandwidth can provide. To address this issue, basic proxy caching (Gwertzman and Seltzer 1996; Dingle and Partl 1997; Duska et al. 1997) and prefetching (Duchamp 1999; Griggioen and Appleton 1996; Kroeger et al. 1997; Padmanabhan and Mogul 1996) are often used. Most of these mechanisms optimize caching performance based on object and byte hit ratios. While these two parameters might reflect the network usage, they might not be translated *directly* into user's retrieval latency.

Figure 3.1 shows the object and byte retrieval times for different object sizes respectively. The data are summarized from the actual proxy trace published by the NLANAR (TRACE 2001), which is one of the most standard, up-to-date, real proxy trace sets used in the research community of web caching. Figure 3.1 (a) confirms the random nature of user's retrieval latency of web object (i.e. one miss) due to wide variation of object size, network and server workload, and the physical distance between a web client and a server. Figure 3.1 (b) shows that due to the time required for the TCP connection, the byte retrieval time actually drops for objects with larger size. This observation is actually not surprising because similar conclusion about the insufficiency of cache hit ratio to reflect the processor performance is also reported in computer architecture research.

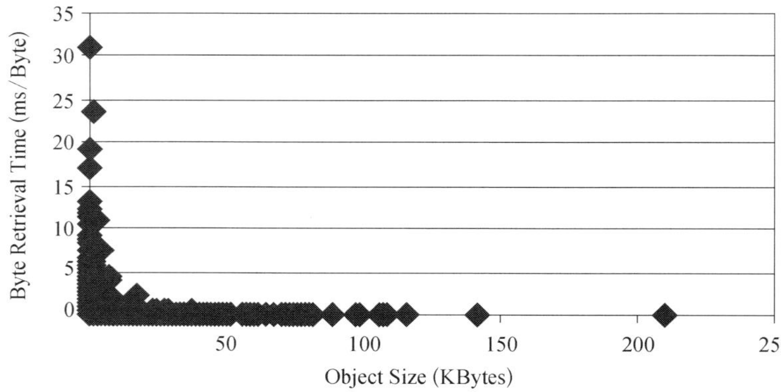

(a)

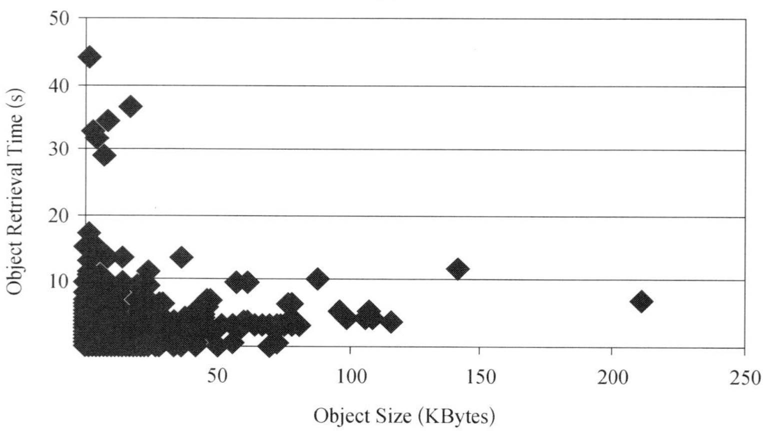

(b)

Fig. 3.1 Current web latency measurement
(a) Object Retrieval Time w.r.t. Object Size; (b) Byte Retrieval Time w.r.t. Object Size.

Parallel fetching of objects for a web page request further complicates the situation. The resulting overlapping of web object retrieval latency makes the prediction of page retrieval time using object or byte hit ratio even more difficult. In fact, it is possible for the fetching of one more object to have no effect on the overall page retrieval time. This motivates us to look for a more accurate timing model to understand web page retrieval latency from a client's viewpoint.

With the maturity of active proxy techniques, a new direction of content delivery is to migrate selected server and browser functionalities into network proxy (ICAP 2010a; OPES 2001). One important concern of this intermediary approach is the latency overhead incurred, especially if the migrated function is related to content optimization for faster web delivery. Depending on how streaming web data is handled by the transformation modules of the intermediary services in the network, its impact on the page retrieval latency might vary tremendously. Hence, it is very important to understand the relationship between the streaming nature of web data and user's experienced page retrieval latency.

In this chapter, we propose a chunk-level latency dependence model (C-LDM) to describe how the interaction among the streaming web data transfer, the HTTP protocol, and the web page structure contributes latency to web page retrieval. By chunk level, we refer to the basic unit of data size streaming from one level of the network gateway to the next level at the HTTP level. Both the browser view and the proxy view of web page retrieval latency are investigated. We show that for typical network connectivity, page retrieval latency is mainly caused by the retrieval dependence among data chunks of a web page container object (e.g. HTML object of the page) and its embedded objects and this is closely related to the content structure of the page. Such understanding is important because it opens opportunities to improve the retrieval speed of web surfing through minimization of data chunk dependence. Once this is done, it also gives another dimension of potential retrieval speed improvement by increasing the parallelism width of the browser for simultaneous object fetching.

In this chapter, wherever is appropriate, we will use latency to refer to user's experienced latency time. Also, for the simplicity of discussion, we assume that no proxy cache is used in the network. Note that the presence of proxy only changes the degree of the latency time without affecting the validity of our model.

3.2 Basic Latency Dependence Model

In this section, we are going to propose the basic concept of latency dependence model as the means to understand how time is spent in object retrieval for a web page request and how it is experienced by a web client.

Before we go into the model, however, it is necessary to have some basic understanding of how a web server streams the requested data to a client upon a page request (Krishnamurthy and Rexford 2001). When a web surfer submits a request, in the form of an URL address, to a web server, reply header and data corresponding to the requested object will be streamed to the client chuck by chunk. The size of data chunks in an object retrieval is not fixed; it depends on the workload of the web server and the network. Nevertheless, according to the properties of the TCP connection and web server, the distribution of chunk size should be around 1.3 Kbytes. More importantly, when a chunk of data is received on the client side, it will be interpreted and further retrieval of *new* web objects that are specified in that data chunk might be triggered.

To get an in-depth understanding of how the retrieval of individual objects in a web page depends on each other and how their object retrieval times contribute to the overall page retrieval time, we propose the chunk-level latency dependence model (C-LDM). The basic idea behind this model is to map retrieval dependence among data chunks of objects in a web page into a directed graph, called the chunk-level latency dependence graph (C-LDG). A node in a C-LDG represents a data chunk of some embedded object in a page and a directed edge represents the retrieval dependence between two data chunks. Properties derived from the graph have direct implications on how latency is experienced by a client. Different from other people's work, we choose to work on the fine-grain chunk level instead of the object level because this can give a more realistic description about the streaming nature of web data and the dependence among themselves.

First, let us precisely define some of the terms used in the latency dependence graph.

Definition 3.1: Page Request

Given an URL address A, its corresponding web page Page_Req (A), as seen by a web client, is made up of a sequence of Nu_Obj (A) objects:

$$\text{Page\_Req}(A) = \{\text{Obj}_0(A),\ \text{Obj}_1(A),\ \text{Obj}_2(A),\ \cdots,\ \text{Obj}_i(A),\ \cdots,\ \text{Obj}_{\text{Nu\_Obj-1}(A)}\}$$

where $\text{Obj}_i(A)$ is an embedded object inside the page and $0 \leqslant i < \text{Nu\_Obj}(A)$.

The order of this sequence follows the order that the objects are defined in a web page.

Definition 3.2: Page Container Object

The container object Pri_Obj (A) of a page request Page_Req (A) is defined as the object that is associated with the page URL address A in the file storage.

Based on the page request definition above, Object_0 is the Pri_Obj of a Page_Req. When Nu_Obj is greater than one, the Pri_Obj will be the basic html, in which all embedded objects in the page are defined. The concept of page container object is very important because all embedded objects inside the page are triggered either directly or indirectly through its retrieval. In other words, there is *strong* retrieval dependence between container and non-container objects.

Definition 3.3: Chunk Transfer Sequence

Given a web object Obj, its transfer from a web server to a client/proxy can be described by an ordered sequence Chunk_Seq of data chunks:

$$\text{Chunk\_Seq}(\text{Obj}) = \{\text{Req}(\text{Obj}),\ \text{Chk}_1(\text{Obj}),\ \text{Chk}_2(\text{Obj}),\ \cdots,\ \text{Chk}_i(\text{Obj}),\ \cdots,\ \text{Chk}_{\text{Chk\_Nu}(\text{Obj})}(\text{Obj})\}$$

where Req (Obj) is the object request sent to a web server, $\text{Chk}_i(\text{Obj})$ is a data chunk of Obj, Chk_Nu (Obj) is the number of data chunks returned from the web server in an object transfer, and $1 \leqslant i \leqslant \text{Chk\_Nu}(\text{Obj})$.

Note that for a given object Obj, the value of Chk_Nu (Obj) is not fixed; it depends on the network and server workload. Furthermore, $\text{Chk}_1(\text{Obj})$ contains not only the data of the object body, but also the reply header information of the object request.

To map the detailed process of object retrieval of a web page request into a chunk-level latency dependence graph C-LDG, all unique objects in the page are represented as chunk transfer sequences in C-LDG, with each node representing either an object request Req (Obj) sent to a web server or a data chunk $\text{Chk}_j(\text{Obj})$ returned from a web server. Furthermore, an object appears in a C-LDG only once, independent of its usage frequency in the page. The rationale behind this decision is that subsequent use of the same object in a page does not generate any actual data transfer between a web server and its client.

Definition 3.4: Object Request Node

A node in a C-LDG is said to be an object request node Node(Req(Obj)) if it represents the data transfer of a web object request Req(Obj) sent from a client to a web server. It contains the URL address of a requested web page, together with all the associated request header information.

Assuming no server "push" protocol (Chen et al. 1999) is defined, there is exactly one object request node Node(Req(Obj)) for the chunk transfer sequence of Obj.

Definition 3.5: Data Chunk Node

A node in a C-LDG is said to be a data chunk node Node(Chk_i(Obj)) if it represents the transfer of a data chunk Chk_i of a web object Obj from a web server to a client, and $1 \leqslant i \leqslant$ Chk_Nu(Obj).

For the first returned data chunk Chk_1(Obj) of an object transfer sequence Chunk_Seq(Obj), it also contains the reply header information of the object request.

The latency dependence of data retrieval among object requests and data chunks in a given web page can be described by the directed edges connecting their nodes. In a C-LDG, there are three types of directed edges. They are (i) object queuing edge, (ii) object request edge, and (iii) inter_chunk edge.

Definition 3.6: Object Queuing Edge

A directed edge in a C-LDG is said to be an object queuing edge if it connects a data chunk node Node(Chk_i(Obj_j)) of an object Obj_j to an object request node Node(Req(Obj_k)) of Obj_k, where Obj_j, $Obj_k \in$ Page_Req, $1 \leqslant i \leqslant$ Chk_Nu(Obj_j), and $j \neq k$.

Definition 3.7: Object Request Edge

A directed edge in a C-LDG is said to be an object request edge if it connects an object request node Node(Req(Obj)) of a web object sequence Chunk_Seq(Obj) to the first returned data chunk node Node(Chk_1(Obj)) of the same sequence.

Definition 3.8: Inter_Chunk Edge

A directed edge in a C-LDG is said to be an inter_chunk edge if it connects two successive data chunk nodes Node(Chk_i) and Node(Chk_{i+1}) of the same object Obj, where $1 \leqslant i <$ Chk_Nu(Obj).

The first type of edges, object queuing edge, represents the queuing of a web object request to be sent out on the client side once the object demand is made known to the client (probably through the interpretation of some data chunk content). The second type of edges, object request edge, represents the sending of an object request by a web client to the receiving of the first data chunk of the object, including the reply header information, from a web server. The third type of edges, the inter_chunk edge, represents the receiving of successive data chunks of a requested object. The retrieval dependence and straight ordering relationship among object request nodes and data chunk nodes are captured by the direction of the edges connecting them in the C-LDG. Furthermore, the principle of transitivity applies.

Theorem 3.1: Principle of Transitivity

In a C-LDG, if Node_i depends on Node_j and Node_j depends on Node_k, then Node_i depends on Node_k, where Node_i, Node_j, and Node_k can be object request node or data chunk.

The latency time gap between the transfer of two successive object request/chunks is represented by the weight of the edge connecting them in the C-LDG.

Definition 3.9: Weight of an Edge

In a C-LDG, the weight of an edge $<\text{Node}_i, \text{Node}_j>$ represents the latency time gap between the completion of data transfer for Node_i and Node_j, where Node_i and Node_j can be request object node or data chunk node.

The term "completion" for an object request node refers to the sending out of the object request from a web client whereas "completion" for a data chunk node refers to the receiving of a data chunk by a web client.

Definition 3.10: In-Degree of a Node in C-LDG

The in-degree of a node *i* in a C-LDG represents the number of object requests and/or data chunks that cause the triggering of data transfer for node *i*.

Theorem 3.2: Single Value of In-Degree of C-LDG Nodes

Given a node in a C-LDG, there is exactly one incoming edge to the node. The only exception is the root (or the starting) of the C-LDG, where the in-degree is zero.

This theorem is based on the characteristics of the HTTP protocol and proxy caching. Once a request for a web object is sent out, all subsequent accesses to the object within the same page will be fetched from the local cache. There will not be any triggering of data transfer between a web client and a web server for the reuse of an object.

Definition 3.11: Out-Degree of a Node in C-LDG

The out-degree of a node *i* in a C-LDG represents the the number of embedded object requests that are triggered through the interpretation of data in node *i*. A value "1" needs to be added to the out-degree if node *i* is not a leave node because it represents the implicit next data chunk node of the currently fetched object that will be transferred to a web client after the current one.

The out-degree of an object request node in a C-LDG is equal to one under normal situation because current HTTP protocol uses the single mapping of one request to one object. However, this might change if pushing technologies such as push protocol (Chen et al. 1999) and volume-bundle protocol are used.

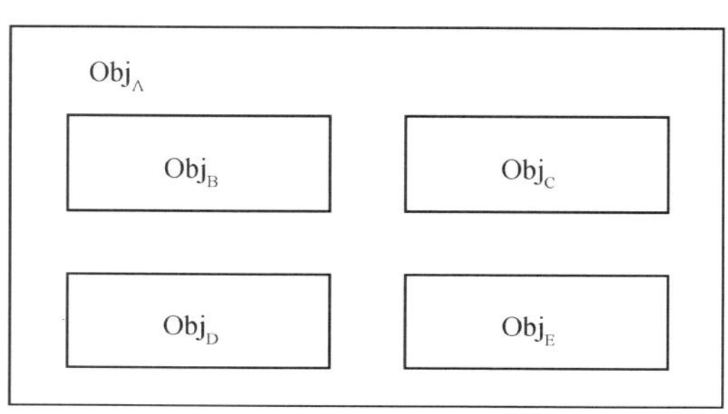

Fig. 3.2 A sample web page with Obj_A as Pri_Obj and four embedded objects Obj_B, Obj_C, Obj_D and Obj_E

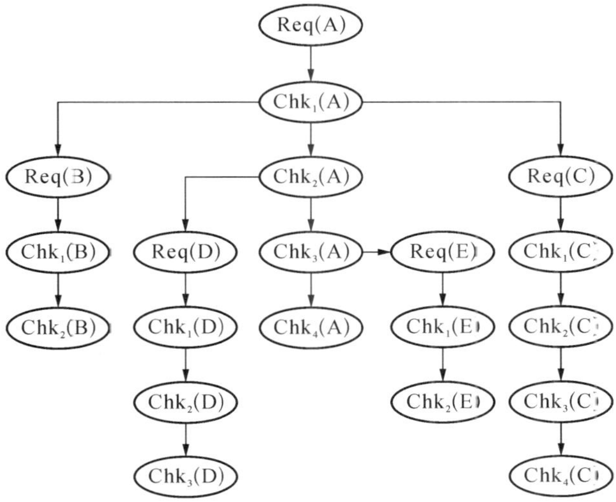

Fig. 3.3 C-LDG for retrieval of web page in Fig. 3.2

With the basic understanding of the properties of nodes and edges in the C-LDM, the C-LDG graph for a web page retrieval can be obtained by monitoring the timing of all unique object transfer sequences associated with a page and by understanding the dependence and triggering action among data chunks and object requests in it. As an illustration, Fig. 3.2 shows a web page with four embedded objects and Fig. 3.3 shows its C-LDG graph. Note that due to the single value of in-degree of C-LDG nodes, C-LDG is always a tree with Node(Req(Pri_Obj)) as the root. Be noted that this model can be easily used to describe normal web documents. For example, the Obj_A can be an HTML file, Obj_B, Obj_C and Obj_D are 2 embedded objects, and Obj_E is a tracker application.

3.3 Web Page Retrieval Latency

In Section 3.2, the basic latency dependence model for web page retrieval is described. Now, we can proceed to an in-depth analysis of how latency time is introduced into web object/page retrieval and is experienced by a web client.

First, let us precisely define the page retrieval time:

Definition 3.12: Page Retrieval Time

The retrieval time of a web page, as is experienced by a web client, is defined as the time from the sending of a request for the container object of the page to the receiving of the last data chunk of the latest arrival object in the page.

There is controversy about the appropriateness of using "complete" page retrieval time as the measurement parameter instead of the "perceived" page retrieval latency. With pros and cons for each parameter, we choose the former one because of the following reasons. Perceived latency of an object only describes the transfer delay of the first data chunk of an object returned from the web server. The size of the object can not be taken into consideration. A more important concern, however, is the focus of this chapter, which is the page retrieval time instead of the object retrieval time. At this moment, the definition of retrieval latency of a *page* is still ambiguous. Due to the partial ordering of embedded object retrieval for a web page, the objects defined in the front part of the page template are likely to have completed their retrieval when the first data chunk of those objects defined at the end of the template arrives at the client. This makes experimentation and comparison difficult because the amount of data transferred for a given page request is not fixed. It is related to the number of objects completely transferred to the client, which will likely depend on the testing environment such as the parallelism width for simultaneous object fetching. An alternate suggestion for "page latency" is to ignore the chunk nodes Chk_i from the C-LDG when i is greater than 1. The drawback of this approach is that the dependence relationship among data chunks of different objects in a page might not be very clear.

Similar argument applies to the interception of web page retrieval. Although it is possible to stop an object or page retrieval in the middle of its transfer and jump to the next page, there is no commonly agreed mechanism to describe this non-deterministic behavior.

Note, however, although we use the "complete" page retrieval time as our measurement parameter, a web client still views the page data in the streaming, chunk-by-chunk manner. There is no change to his perceived time of objects.

Based on the above definition, we can easily see that the retrieval time of a page A is defined by the longest path length starting at the object request node for the container object Req(Pri_Obj(A)) of A (i.e. the root) in the directed C-LDG. Note that the term "longest" here is defined in terms of the weight of edges along the path but not the number of nodes.

To gain insight into how dependence among object requests and data chunks affects page latency, we need to understand the intrinsic meanings and implications of the three types of edges found in a C-LDG.

An object queuing edge describes the ordering of receiving a data chunk and sending out a new object request triggered by that chunk. Hence, its weight denotes the queuing time of sending out an embedded object request to a web server once its demand is known to a web client through the interpretation of the current data chunk. Its value is mainly affected by the object retrieval parallelism available on the web client side, and the number and latency of object requests that have been triggered previously.

An object request edge describes the ordering of sending out an object request and receiving the reply header and perhaps some data body of the requested object. Thus, its weight captures the latency time in setting up the TCP connection between a web client and a web server and getting the first data chunk of the requested object back. It is affected by the workload of the web server and the network bandwidth availability as well as the persistence of the network connection that might be established by previous object requests.

An inter_chunk edge describes the ordering of getting two successive chunks of data of a requested object back to a web client, assuming that the TCP connection between the client and the web server has already been set up through prior data chunk transfer from the same object/site. Unlike the object request edge, its weight is mainly affected by the size of the data chunk and the workload of the web server and the network.

Relative to the starting of retrieval of a requested page (i.e. sending out an object request for the container object Req (Pri_Obj (A)) of Page A), the latency of an object retrieval can be described by four components. They are definition time, queuing time, connection time, and chunk sequence time. The sequence order of these four components as well as their relationship with the page retrieval time is shown in Fig. 3.4. Note that the starting point of the object retrieval time is always the same as that of the page retrieval time.

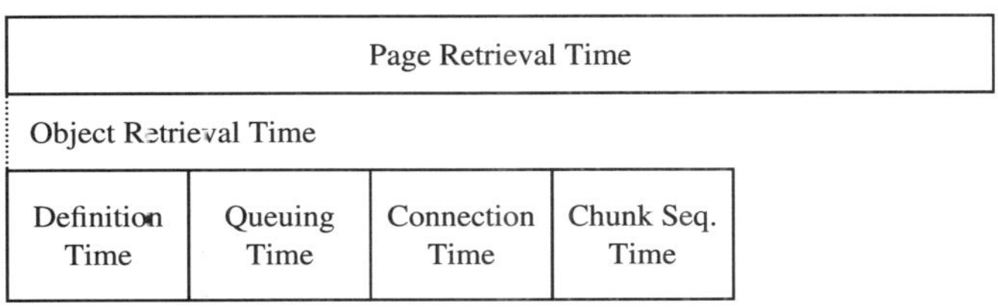

Fig. 3.4 Relationship of four components of latency time with page retrieval time

Definition 3.13: Object Definition Time (DT)

Given the retrieval for a web page A, the definition time of an object Obj_i in A is defined as the time between sending out a request for the container object Req (Pri_Obj (A)) and receiving a data chunk $Chk_j(Obj_k)$ that triggers the request for object Obj_i, where Obj_i, $Obj_k \in$ Page_Req (A) and $i \neq k$.

In the C-LDG, the definition time of an object Obj is given by the path length from the object request node for the page container object to a data chunk node in some object transfer sequence that connects to the object request node for Obj.

This definition time signifies the importance of the position in the container object of a web page where an embedded object in the page is defined. It specifies the earliest time that an embedded object request can be made known to a web client. This puts a lower bound to the retrieval time of an object with respect to the starting time of a page request. Furthermore, the effect of definition time on page retrieval latency is quite sensitive to the parallelism width for object fetching. As the parallelism width increases, the definition time will play a more important role in determining the overall page retrieval latency. This will be discussed later in Section 3.4.

Definition 3.14: Object Queuing Time (QT)

Given the retrieval for a web page A, the queuing time of an object Obj is defined as the latency between the time when the existence/demand of Obj is known to a web client to the time the object request for Obj is sent out, where Obj $\in$ Page_Req (A).

In the C-LDG, this queuing time for an object Obj is given by the weight of the object queuing edge from the data chunk node that defines Obj to the object request node for Obj.

This queuing time exists mainly due to the lack of parallelism for object retrieval. It is generally agreed that a significant portion of web pages on the Internet is made up of more than four objects. As an example, www.cnn.com has more than 50 objects in its home page. However, current web browsers, both Netscape and MS IE, allow object retrieval parallelism of four only. As a result, the phenomenon of object queuing on the client side occurs.

Definition 3.15: Connection Time (CT)

Given the retrieval for a web page A, the connection time of an object Obj is defined as the latency time from sending out the request for Obj to receiving the first data chunk of the reply for Obj.

In the C-LDG, the connection time for the retrieval of an object Obj is given by the weight of the object request edge from the object request node Node (Req (Obj)) to the first data chunk node Node (Chk_1 (Obj)) in the object transfer sequence Chunk_Seq (Obj).

This connection time is basically made up of three portions: (i) the time to set up the connection between a web client and a web server, (ii) the time for an object request to be received by a web server, and (iii) the time to retrieve the reply header of the request and perhaps some data body in the requested object. As a result, it is affected by the persistence of the network connection with respect to prior requests to the same server. Under the persistent HTTP/1.1 (Krishnamurthy and Rexford 2001), we expect that the connection time for the container object in a requested page should be higher than those for embedded objects in the page, provided that they all come from the same server.

Definition 3.16: Chunk Sequence Time (CST)

Given the retrieval for a web page A, the chunk sequence time of an object Obj is defined as the latency time after the receiving of the first data chunk Chk_1 (Obj) to the receiving of the last data chunk $Chk_{Chk\_Nu(obj)}$ (Obj) in its object transfer sequence Chunk_Seq (Obj), where Chk_Nu (Obj) is the number of data chunks returned from a web server for Obj.

In the C-LDG, the chunk sequence time for an object Obj is given by the path length from Node (Chk_1 (Obj)) to Node ($Chk_{Chunk\_Nu(Obj)}$ (Obj)) in the object transfer sequence Chunk_Seq (Obj).

This last component for the object retrieval latency is the time consumed in the actual transfer of the data body of a requested object. Clearly, it will be affected by the size of the object as well as the workload of the server and the network.

With the above definitions, we see that the definition time component of an embedded object in a page actually carries the DT, QT, CS and part of CST delay of its ancestor objects defining it. Hence, this gives an accurate description about the relationship of retrieving an embedded object in a web page with respect to its page structure and order.

Table 3.1 Factors Affecting Each of Four Components of Web Object Retrieval Time

	DT	**QT**	**CT**	**CST**
Network Bandwidth	X	X	X	X
Object Size (current)				X
Object Size (ancestors)	X	X		
Number of Objects		X		
Persistence			X	
Obj. Position in Page	X			
Retrieval Parallelism		X		

Table 3.1 gives a summary of the factors that affect the four components of object retrieval time. Using the example used in the last section(Figs. 3.2 and 3.3), the four components of the fourth embedded object D are shown in Fig. 3.5. Note that there is always one object in a requested page with object retrieval time equal to the page retrieval time.

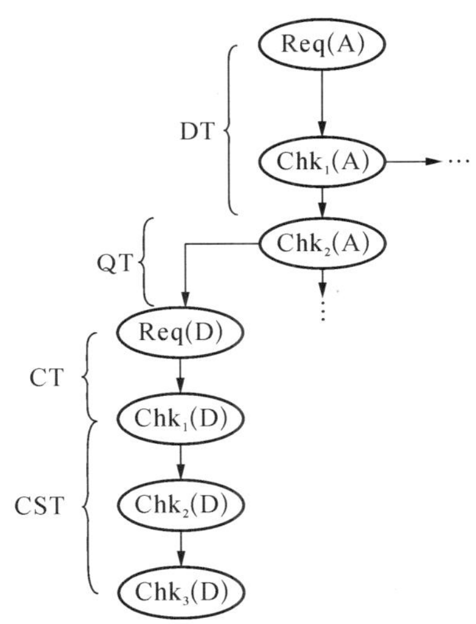

Fig. 3.5 Four components of latency time for object D

3.4 Experimental Study and Analysis

To illustrate the importance of the C-LDM, we would like to use it to study the actual time spent on web page retrieval and to analyze its relationship with the parallelism width for object fetching and the definition dependence among data chunks of objects.

3.4.1 Experimental Environment

To analyze the web page latency based on our proposed latency dependence model,

URL addresses of web pages are sampled from the proxy traces available from NLANR (TRACE 2001). These traces are used because they are the most popular, up-to-date, real proxy traces available to the research community of web content delivery and caching for experimentation and comparison. One day trace in November, 2001 is randomly chosen for the study. The URLs contained in this trace has no preference and perfect in the means of "random".

For each sampled web page, its retrieval is repeated from the Singapore Advanced Research Network in the National University of Singapore, which has 45 Mbits link to the U.S. All triggering actions of embedded objects in a web page and their timing measurements are recorded in a monitoring proxy at the data chunk level on the client side.

3.4.2 Web Page Latency Breakdown

First, let us look at the relative distribution of the four components of latency in web object retrieval. Figure 3.6 plots their relative distribution percentages against the definition order number of embedded objects in a web page.

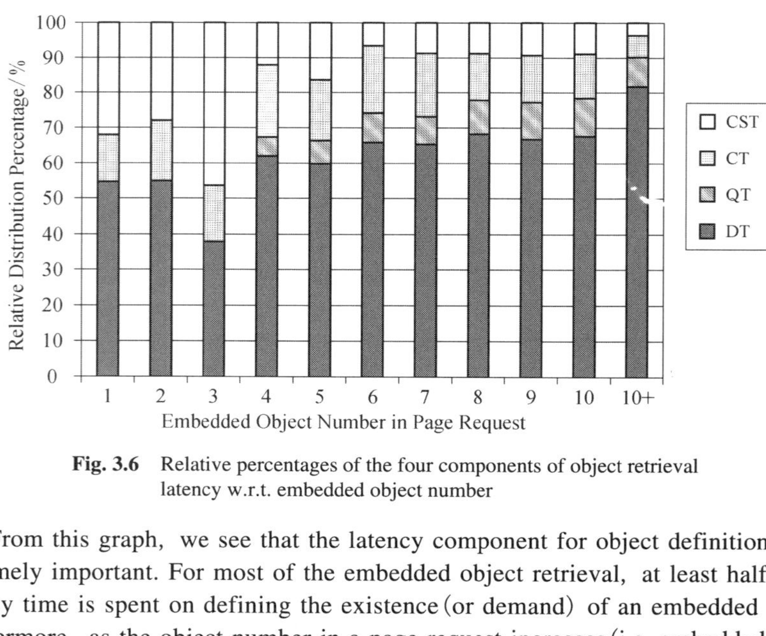

Fig. 3.6 Relative percentages of the four components of object retrieval latency w.r.t. embedded object number

From this graph, we see that the latency component for object definition DT is extremely important. For most of the embedded object retrieval, at least half of the latency time is spent on defining the existence (or demand) of an embedded object. Furthermore, as the object number in a page request increases (i.e. embedded object defined towards the end of the page container object), the definition time is increased to over 80% of the object retrieval time.

This observation is surprising, as one might expect the actual data transfer times, CT and CST, to be the dominating ones. The result actually points out one important fact about web page retrieval. The definition time of an embedded object in a web page carries the DT, QT, CT, and part of CST of all its dependent ancestors and this is related to the web page structure and the declaration of resource usage in a page (just like variable declaration in programming languages). This gives hints to a new direction of improving the performance of web page retrieval. If the existence of embedded objects in a page can be made known to a web client at the beginning of a page, significant reduction in their definition time and in turn the relative object retrieval latency (with respect to page retrieval latency) can be obtained. Techniques to achieve this will be discussed in detail in next chapter.

About the queuing time QT in object retrieval latency, the graph shows that it is zero for embedded object sequence number less than four. The explanation for this phenomenon is that the maximum parallelism width for object fetching defined internally in most common browsers such as Microsoft IE and Netscape is four[1]. Hence, there is no lack of parallelism, the and queuing of object requests on the client side will not happen. Beyond this point, the relative QT increases with the embedded object sequence number, up to about 10% of the object retrieval latency. This is reasonable because the chance of accumulating object requests is higher towards the end of the page container object than at its beginning. With 5% to 10% of the overall object retrieval latency spent on object request queuing, it gives potentials to improve web latency through the increase of object fetch parallelism.

The connection time CT is shown to be 6% to 17% of the web object retrieval latency. This confirms the importance of persistence of network connection and explains why keeping the network connection to a web site alive can improve the latency time. Finally, the chunk sequence time CST is observed to drop from over 30% to a few percent with the increase in embedded object sequence number. While its absolute value does not change, its relative portion in web object retrieval time decreases due to the significant increase in DT and QT. Nevertheless, it is small when compared with DT.

The above analysis shows that the lack of declaration of embedded object usage in the beginning of a page container object and the limited parallelism for object fetching are the two main causes for web object retrieval latency. To relate this result to page retrieval latency, Fig. 3.7 shows the distribution of relative object retrieval time (DT +T+CT+CST) and transfer time (CT+CST) with respect to page retrieval latency. We see that while the relative ratio of object retrieval time against page retrieval time is more or less evenly distributed, the curve shifts significantly to the left if the definition and queuing times DT and QT are taken out. This shows their importance in contributing to page retrieval time. Since DT and QT are not related to the network bandwidth availability, this gives a new direction for improving web latency, by making use of embedded objects known to a web client earlier and by increasing the parallelism width for simultaneous object fetching.

---

[1] Note that common browsers set the maximum parallelism width to four for object fetching because of cost-effective reason. Due to the streaming nature of data chunks and the dependence among them, increasing the parallelism width might not give substantial performance gain(see Fig. 3.10 in Section 3.4.3 below), but it might overload the server easily. However, with the increasing demand from clients and web servers for better web service quality and the techniques proposed in Chapter, 4, the above argument needs to be re-evaluated.

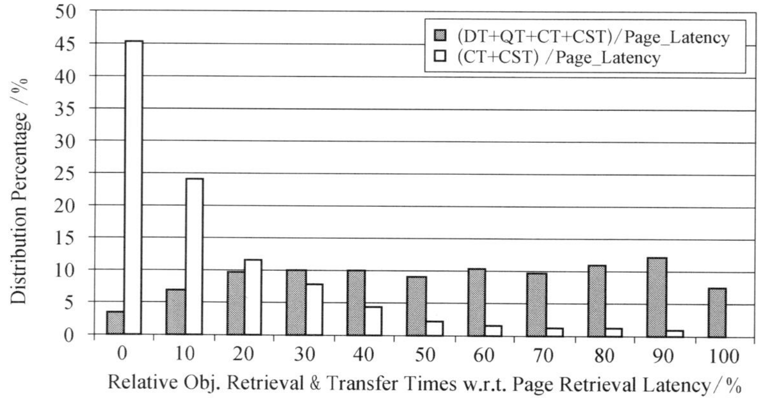

Fig. 3.7 Distribution of relative object retrieval and transfer times w.r.t. page retrieval latency

3.4.3 Object Retrieval Parallelism

In this section, we would like to study the effect of parallelism width for simultaneous object fetching on page retrieval time.

Figure 3.8 shows the distribution of number of objects in a web page. We see that while there are web pages made of one single object, there are about half of the web pages with substantially more objects inside, with an average number of 3.84 objects per page. For those web pages with multiple objects, increasing the parallelism width for simultaneously object fetching should have positive effect on web page retrieval latency.

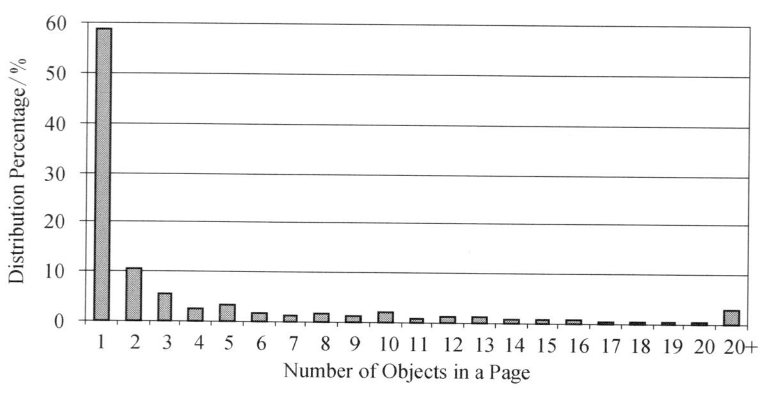

Fig. 3.8 Number of objects in a web page

We would also like to study the relative percentages of the latency time spent on queuing (QT), as compared to the actual data transfer times (CT+CST). Figure 3.9 plots the relative timing of queuing, connection and chunk sequence transfer times against web object size.

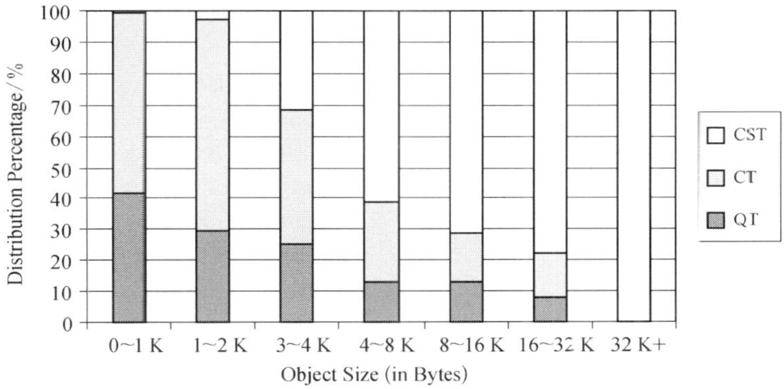

Fig. 3.9 Relative percentages of latency of QT, CT and CST w.r.t. object size

When the object size is small, the queuing time is relatively quite high. These objects are likely small embedded objects such as GIF defined in the middle of the page container object body. With the limited retrieval parallelism of 4, the queuing time might be 10% to 40% of the relative object retrieval time (once the object existence is known to a client). As the object size increases, the relative percentage of the object retrieval time spent in queuing decreases. This is expected because more time is now spent on the actual transfer of data chunks. Note that while the relative queuing time decreases, its absolute value is actually more or less the same. Beyond the object size of 32 Kbytes, the queuing time is zero. Further study shows that most of them are actually single object pages such as JPEG.

Figure 3.10 shows the effect of increasing the parallelism width for simultaneous object fetch. With about half of the web pages having multiple objects inside a page, page retrieval latency is expected to decrease with increasing parallelism width. However, instead of getting the expected performance gain, the graph shows that the performance gain beyond the parallelism of 4 is very little. The observation is valid even if the parallelism width is unlimited.

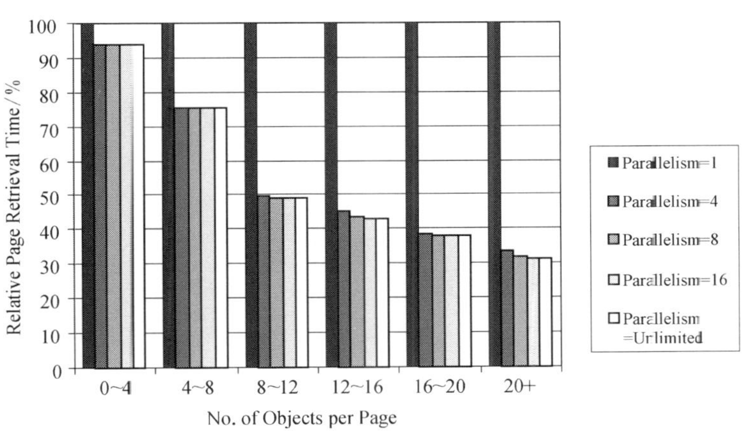

Fig. 3.10 Relative page retrieval time w.r.t. number of objects in a page under different parallelism width

This result is quite surprising, as there are many pages with more than four objects inside. Further study gives the explanation behind. Many objects are triggered in the middle of the page container object retrieval. The average out-degree of data chunk nodes in the chunk transfer sequence is shown in Fig.3.11, with an average value of 1.396. Figure 3.12 plots the same graph as in Fig. 3.11, except that the percentage of object body retrieved is used instead of the chunk sequence number in an object transfer. Taking the default next chunk away in the discussion, the number of new embedded objects defined per data chunk is actually not very high. With fair evenly distributed number of embedded objects defined in each data chunk of the chunk transfer sequence of the page container object, the demand for wider object fetch parallelism is not high. Increase in parallelism helps very little in this case because there are embedded objects with definition point only at the end of the container object transfer.

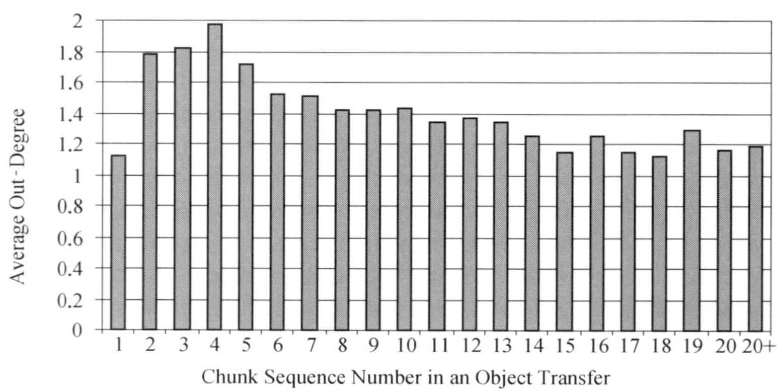

Fig. 3.11 Average out-degree of nodes w.r.t. chunk sequence number in an object transfer

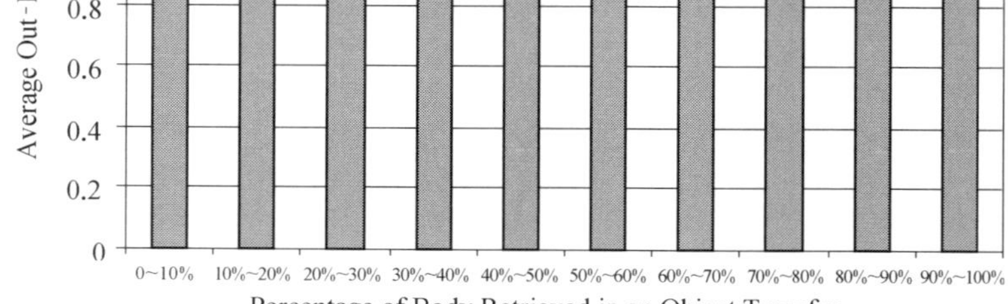

Fig. 3.12 Average out-degree of nodes w.r.t. the percentage of body retrieved in an object transfer

The observation here raises one important issue in web performance. Mapping object retrieval time to page retrieval time is a very complex task, and it depends on the dependence among object requests and data chunks of objects in a page. Techniques that can improve object retrieval time might not improve the page retrieval time. In the case of object retrieval parallelism, we will see in the next chapter that if it works together with the rescheduling of objects retrieval by declaring the embedded objects in the beginning of the page container object, parallelism effect can take place much more effectively.

3.4.4 Definition Time and its Rescheduling

Section 3.4.2 shows the importance of definition time in web object retrieval latency. In this section, we would like to have an in-depth investigation on how embedded objects are defined in different data chunks of a page container object. Based on our study, we would also like to explore the possibility of regaining performance through the reposition of definition points of embedded objects in the page container object of a web request.

Figure 3.13 shows the distribution of number of data chunks per object, with an average value of 4.15. Here we see that about half of the web objects under study are made up of multiple data chunks. Together with the in-degree of nodes in the C-LDG shown in Figs. 3.11 and 3.12, the opportunity of reducing object retrieval latency by promoting the definition point of embedded objects to the earlier data chunk of the page container object is obvious. Furthermore, if only the page container objects are considered, the distribution curve is actually found to shift to the right, with more data chunks per object.

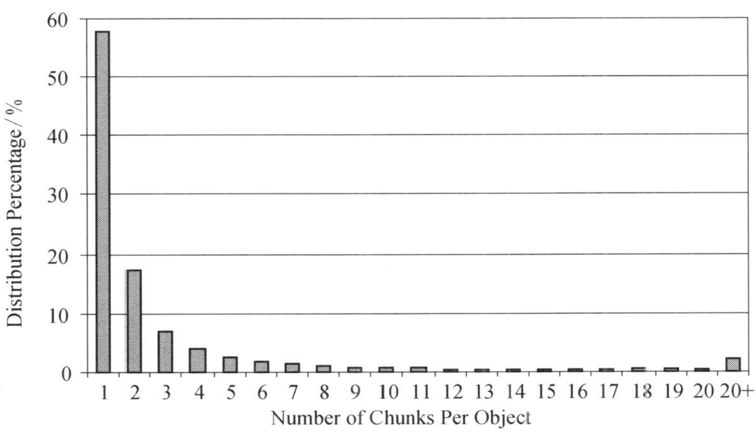

Fig. 3.13 Distribution of number of chunks per object

Figure 3.14 gives the distribution of data chunk size. It shows that the average chunk size is about 1.35 Kbytes, which is in agreement with the TCP and network properties. (Krishnamurthy and Rexford 2001).

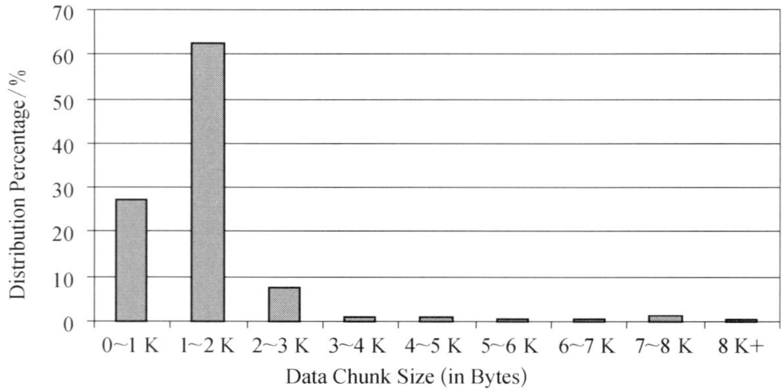

Fig. 3.14 Distribution of data chunk size

With reference to Fig.3.6, we already showed that the definition time for object retrieval is very important, occupying 50% to 80% of its latency. By repositioning the starting node of object queuing edge for new embedded object retrieval to the beginning data chunk node of the page container object, significant performance improvement is expected. Figure 3.15 shows the relative page retrieval time with respect to the number of objects per page under different definition positions in the container object. In particular, we would like to study the effect of declaring the usage of embedded objects in a page at the request node of its container object Node(Req(Pri_Obj)). This is what we call the "**push-forward**" effect.

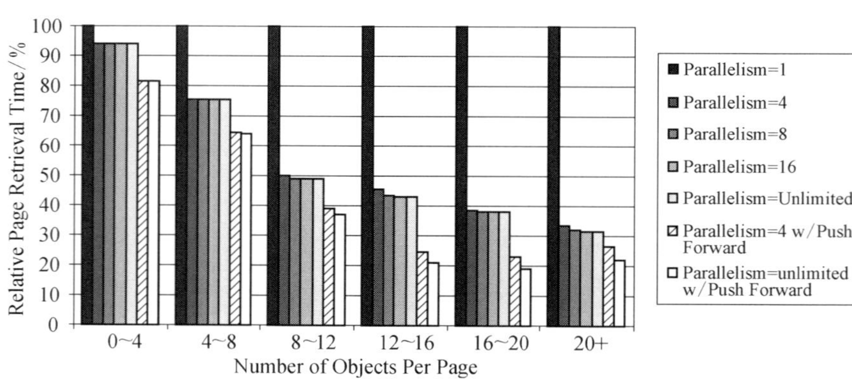

Fig. 3.15 Relative page retrieval time w.r.t. number of objects per page under different obj. definition positions

Figure 3.15 clearly shows that the push-forward effect can bring in huge improvement in page retrieval latency. Table 3.2 summaries the improvement of latency reduction due to the push-forward effect on embedded objects. When the parallelism width for object fetching is 4, pushing can bring in page retrieval latency reduction ranging from 13.5% to 45.9%. Even more interesting observation is made when the parallelism width is increased to unlimited. Unlike the negligible result reported in

Section 3.4.3, the latency reduction now ranges from 13.5% to 53.7%. Here we show that pushing the definition point of embedded objects forward can provide a better environment for parallel object fetching to work. This is quite reasonable because once the embedded objects in a page are made known to a client at the beginning of a page, part of the performance bottleneck will be shifted to the availability of parallelism for object fetching. With the push-forward effect, larger improvement is observed for pages with more objects than those with fewer objects when the parallelism width for object fetching is increased.

Table 3.2 Page Latency Reduction Due to "Push-Forward" Effect on Embedded Objects

No. of Objects Per Page	Latency Reduction Due to "Push-Forward" Effect, Parallelism width =		Additional Latency Reduction due to Increase in Parallelism
	4	Unlimited	
0~4	13.5%	13.5%	0.00%
5~8	14.5%	15.4%	0.90%
9~12	21.9%	26.4%	4.50%
13~16	45.9%	53.7%	7.81%
17~20	40.4%	50.8%	10.43%
20+	21.8%	34.3%	12.48%

3.5 Discussion about Validity of Observed Results Under Different Environments

Up to now, we have presented a detailed analysis of the chunk-level user's experienced latency in a typical network environment. In this section, we would like to discuss what happens to our model and results if parameters in our testing environment change.

The first concern is about the effect of object pipelining and persistent connection. Definitely, techniques can improve the page retrieval latency. However, they should not replace the usefulness of having parallel object fetching. The two techniques are just two different dimensions of improving the user's retrieval latency and they are actually complementary to each other.

The second concern is about the effect of forward proxy caching and content distribution network services. While the C-LDM is not changed, the absolute values of the four components of latency will be affected. More specifically, forward proxy caching will affect the CT and CST, which in turns, affects DT and QT. However, since the latency in this case should not be a concern to web clients, there lacks interest to go into detailed discussion of this case. In the C-LDM, if an object can be retrieved to a client with negligible latency, as an approximation, it can be ignored from the C-LDG.

The third question is about the effect of having a dominating performance bottleneck. This includes the retrieval of a very large web object (such as a streaming video file) and the use of a very slow modem link. In both cases, the CST component will clearly be the primary dominating factor to latency. This also implies that bandwidth availability and content encoding scheme will still be more important than the web page structure nor object definition position in a page template. In the case of very large object size, intra-object parallelism for simultaneous multiple range streaming for the same object should be investigated. Note that it is worth mentioning that current web traffic is still dominated by texts and images.

The fourth question is about the effect of the size of the page template (or container object of a web page) on the result of the "push-forward" effect observed in Section 3.4.4. With a smaller container object size, its effectiveness will definitely be reduced. While there are container objects of web pages with small sizes, there also exist those (such as index pages) with larger sizes. As we will show in next chapter, techniques to achieve the "push-forward" effect can achieve significant improvement in web caching and content delivery performance. Furthermore, it is worth mentioning that most objects with only one data chunk reported in Fig. 3.13 are found to be GIF objects instead of the container objects of web pages.

Finally, as is reported in Fig. 3.8 in Section 3.4.3, about half of the pages under study have only one object inside. In this case, parallel object fetching will not have any effect on them. However, just like the above argument on the page template size, it does not affect our overall observation, as there are another half of the pages for potential improvement.

3.6 Conclusion

In this chapter, we propose a fine-grain latency dependence model to understand how retrieval latency of individual objects in a web page contributes to the final page retrieval latency. We observe that the definition time for the existence of an embedded object and the queuing time for sending out the object request are the two main components of both object and page retrieval latency. We also show that simply increasing the parallelism for simultaneously object fetching is not effective because the embedded objects might not be defined in time to take advantage of the parallelism. Finally, we show the potentials of the "push-forward" effect of reducing web page retrieval latency. Web page retrieval latency can potentially be reduced by 13% to 50%. This motivates us to look for practical solutions to achieve this "pushing-forward" effect in web page retrieval.

References

(Chen et al. 1999) Chen H, Mathur A, Anwar I et al (1999) Wormhole Caching with HTTP PUSH method for a Satellite-Based Global Multicast Replication System. In: Proceedings of the 4th International Web Caching Workshop, San Diego, CA, March 1999

(Dingle and Partl 1997) Dingle A, Partl T(1997) Web Cache Coherence. In: Proceedings of 5th International World Wide Web Conference, Lisbon, Portugal, May 1997

(Duchamp 1999) Duchamp D(1999) Prefetching Hyperlinks. In: Proceedings of USENIX Symposium on Internet Technologies and Systems, Boulder, CO, USA, October 1999

(Duska et al. 1997) Duska B M, Marwood D, Feeley M J(1997) The Measured Access Characteristics of World-Wide-Web Client Proxy Caches. In: Proceedings of USENIX Symposium on Internet Technologies and Systems, Monterey, California, USA, December 1997

(Griggioen and Appleton 1996) Griggioen J, Appleton R(1996) The Design, Implementation, and Evaluation of a Predictive Caching Filing System. In: Technical Report CS-264-96, Department of Computer Science, University of Kentucky, Lexington, KY, USA, June 1996

(Gwertzman and Seltzer 1996) Gwertzman J, Seltzer M(1996) World-Wide-Web Cache Consistency. In: Proceedings of the USENIX Technical Conference, San Diego, CA, USA, 1996

(ICAP 2010a) ICAP-Forum (2010) Internet Content Adaptation Protocol(I-CAP). http: //www.icap-forum.org. Accessed 14 April 2010

(Kroeger et al. 1997) Kroeger T M, Long D E, Mogul J C(1997) Exploring the Bounds of Web Latency Reduction from Caching and Prefetching. In: Proceedings of USENIX Symposium on Internet Technologies and Systems, Monterey, California, USA, December 1997

(Krishnamurthy and Rexford 2001) Krishnamurthy B, Rexford J(2001) Web Protocols and Practice. Addison Wesley, Boston, USA

(OPES 2001) Open Pluggable Edges Services(OPES) (2001) http: //datatracker.ietf.org/wg/opes/charter. Accessed 14 April 2010

(Padmanabhan and Mogul 1996) Padmanabhan V N, Mogul J C(1996) Using Predictive Prefetching to Improve World Wide Web Latency. ACM Computer Review 26(3): 22-36

4

Accelerating Web Page Retrieval Through Reduction in Data Chunk Dependence

4.1 Introduction

The "world-wide-wait" problem is always an important concern to all web content/service providers and clients. Retrieval latency of web page is generally agreed to be a primary criterion to determine the quality of most web services; it is also a determination factor for visitors to return to a web site.

There are two traditional approaches to addressing this "world-wide-wait" problem. The first one is to upgrade the network and content servers. Due to the high cost involved, this option should be considered only if the capacities of the current network bandwidth and servers are fully utilized. The second approach is to deploy proxy caching in the network. With its ability to reuse web data, proxy caching is gaining its popularity in its deployment (Luotonen and Altis 1994; Glassman 1994; Wessels 2001).

It is found, however, that the performance of basic proxy caching is approaching its limit. This is due to the amount of data sharing found in typical web environment. Even for large-scale Internet service providers, the observed cache hit ratio only ranges from about 40% to 50% (IRCAC). The hit ratio drops significantly as the number of clients served by a proxy cache decreases. For example, in typical enterprises and secondary schools with about 500 to 1,000 client users, the observed hit ratio can be as low as 10% to 20% as what have been observed in some Australian high schools.

More importantly, it is found that cache efficiency is bounded by the increasing amount of non-cacheable, dynamically created web content due to security, database and other personalization technologies. Although prefetching (Padmanabhan and Mogul 1996; Kroeger et al. 1997; Duchamp 1999) is sometimes mentioned in literature as a means to hide the retrieval latency of objects, yet due to its excessive bandwidth consumption and low prediction accuracy, its cost-effectiveness is often questionable.

To overcome the performance barrier of web content delivery, researchers recently turn their focus to the acceleration of the first time access of web pages. This direction has huge potentials because it covers all pages and objects, independent of whether they are cacheable or not. Currently, the two main areas of investigation are server-client connectivity and encoding scheme. For server-client connectivity, it covers path routing optimization, pre-establishment of server-client connection (Cohen and Kaplan 2000), and persistent connection (Wang and Cao 1998; HTTP1 1999). For encoding schemes, it investigates data compression (EXPAN 2010), transcoding (Han et al. 1998; Fox and Brewer 1996; Fox et al. 1998), and data compaction (Wills et al. 2001). However, very little research work is found in the literature on accelerating web content delivery by rescheduling the retrieval of embedded objects for a given page request.

In this chapter, we would like to research on the mechanisms to accelerate the first time retrieval of web pages. More specifically, we would like to investigate the potentials and practicability of rescheduling the retrieval of embedded objects for a page request. In the last chapter, we see that a significant amount of latency is introduced to web page retrieval due to the definition for the existence (or usage) of embedded objects in a page and their queuing delay for simultaneous object fetching. To regain the performance, we take a two-step solution to this latency problem. First, we propose mechanisms to allow a client to know the usage of embedded objects in a web page earlier, preferably without the need to fetch the data chunks of the container object that defines them. This can be done by two different mechanisms: (i) object declaration (OD), and (ii) history-based page structure table (PST). Once the knowledge about the usage of embedded objects is available, rescheduling of web object retrieval, together with the increasing parallelism width for simultaneous object fetching, can be used to reduce the retrieval latency of web pages.

Just like the argument given in the last chapter, we will use the retrieval time of a "complete" web page as the primary measurement parameter in our study here. Also, to make the discussion easier, the following terms have to be defined:

- *page latency* to represent the retrieval latency of a complete web page
- *parallelism width* to represent the maximum parallelism width for simultaneous fetching of object for a web page request
- *intra-page rescheduling* to represent the rescheduling of embedded objects fetching for a web page request

The outline of the chapter is as follows. Section 4.2 gives the pre-requistes for rescheduling the retrieval of embedded objects in a page. Then two mechanisms, the object declaration and the history-based page structure table, are proposed in Section 4.3 to pass the information about embedded object usage in a web page to a client earlier than the arrival of data chunks of the page container object defining them. Comparison between these two mechanisms is also given in this section. In Section 4.4, the performance study of the two mechanisms is given. Finally, the chapter ends in Section 4.5.

4.2 Pre-requistes for Rescheduling of Embedded Object Retrieval

First let's have a look of today's Internet browsing. A client usually uses the popular browsers, like IE or Netscape. When he inputs a URL in the browser, the browser will first send the request to the web server and gets the template file, usually the HTML file. Once the file is streaming in, the browser will try to interpret the template and send the request for the embedded objects. The browser has limitations on overall TCP connection numbers for each browsing session.

In order to perform intra-page rescheduling for faster web access, we argue that there are two challenges being faced by the current web environment. They are the lack of advanced information about the embedded object usage in the beginning of a web page request and the limited parallelism width for simultaneous object fetching.

According to the current HTML definition for web structure, a page is made up of a container object Pri_Obj_c, together with zero or multiple embedded objects. The **definition point** of an embedded object Obj_e in a page refers to the point of the first use of Obj_e in the page container object. Due to the streaming nature of web data, a definition latency dependence gap for an embedded object Obj_e in a page exists between the time of sending out a request for its page container object Pri_Obj_c and the time of receiving some data chunk of Pri_Obj_c that contains the definition point of Obj_e. As we discussed in the last chapter, this gap results in the definition time component of object retrieval latency. Depending on the position of the definition point of an embedded object in a web page, its impact to the page retrieval latency can be significant.

Figure 4.1 shows two pages Page1 and Page2 having the same container object size but different definition points for the embedded object Obj_B inside. For Page1 in Fig. 4.1 (a), the use of Obj_B is defined in the first chunk of the page container object whereas for Page2 in Fig. 4.1 (b), its use is defined in the last chunk of the page container object. Due to the different definition positions in the two web pages, Obj_B can be retrieved much earlier for Page1 than for Page2, being fetched immediately after the first chunk (i.e. Chk_1) arrival for Page1 and only fetched immediately after the 4th chunk (i.e. Chk_4) arrival for Page2.

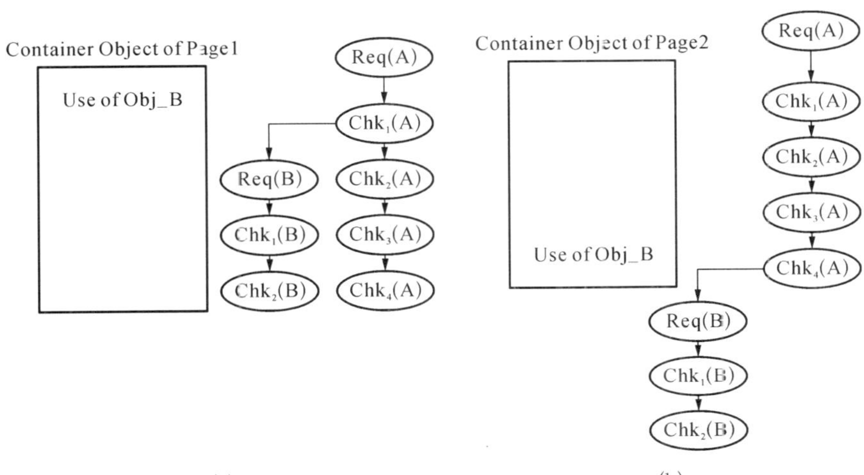

Fig. 4.1 Two web pages having same container object size and embedded object Obj_B and their associated latency dependence graph

This discrepancy of retrieval time for Obj_B occurs because the data of the container object for Page1 and Page2 are streamed to the client chunk by chunk. And a client interprets each chunk of data immediately after he receives it and takes immediate fetching action on the embedded object (s) defined in the chunk. In the current web environment, rescheduling the retrieval of an embedded object earlier than its definition point is difficult because its existence is simply unknown to the previous chunks of the page container object. Referring to the same example in Fig. 4.1 (b), chunk Chk_1 to Chk_3 do not have any information about the definition of Obj_B. Note that the further away (from the beginning) an embedded object is defined in a web page, the larger the expected latency dependence gap for its retrieval will be.

The maximum parallelism width for simultaneous object fetching for a web request is another factor to determine the page retrieval latency. Since the introduction of the world-wide-web, a web page is always broken down into one container object (e.g. HTML) and multiple embedded objects (e.g. GIFs). If there are more requests for embedded objects than the parallelism width can support, queuing will occur. This results in the queuing time component of object retrieval latency described in Chapter 3. It is obvious that the larger the parallelism width is, the shorter the page retrieval latency is expected[1]. Currently, most browsers, including Netscape and Microsoft IE, allow a maximum parallelism width of four for simultaneous object fetching. With a significant amount of web pages having more than three embedded objects, this parallelism width definitely limits the performance of web page retrieval.

Still referring to Fig. 4.1 (a), if the parallelism width is still available during the receipt of Chk_1 of the page container object, the request for Obj_B can be sent out immediately, thus overlapping the fetching times of the page container object and Obj_B. On the other hand, if there is a lack of parallelism width, Obj_B might be fetched only after the complete retrieval of the page container object. In this case, the retrieval times of Page1 and Page2 will be the same, despite the fact that the use of Obj_B is made known to the client earlier for Page1 than for Page2.

From the above discussion, it is quite obvious that these two factors actually reinforce each other to determine the overall page retrieval time. Parallelism shows its full effectiveness only if the information about embedded object usage in a page can be made known to a client as early as possible, ideally at the time of request for the page container object. Early notification of the information about embedded object usage in a page to a client takes up its effect only if there is enough parallelism width for simultaneous object fetching. Perhaps one possible reason for the parallelism width of four in today's browsers might be the lack of information about embedded object usage in the earlier chunks of the page container object.

Note that some people might argue about the use of object pipelining over parallel object fetching. We view these two techniques as complementary to each other instead of replacing one another. This argument can be illustrated in processor design, where

---

[1] Note that while this relationship is valid, it is not a linear curve due to the persistence connection and parallel object fetching for a web page request.

instruction pipelining gives the first dimension of performance improvement and parallel instruction execution with multiple functional units in a processor gives the second dimension of performance improvement.

4.3 Intra-Page Rescheduling for Web Page Retrieval

In this section, we would like to propose two basic "**push-forward**" mechanisms to speed up the retrieval of web pages. By "push-forward", we refer to the situation of passing information about embedded object usage in a web page to a client earlier than the arrival of data chunks of the page container object defining them. They are:

- object declaration (OD), and
- history-based page structure table (PST).

The first mechanism, object declaration, is a server side technique that declares the usage of embedded objects in a web page in the beginning of its container object. It requires assistance from the content provider. The second mechanism, history-based page structure table, is a client side solution that needs to keep track of the page structure of previously referenced web pages in a special-purpose table. Since both mechanisms have pros and cons and each performs better than the other in some predefined situations, they can actually be combined to give the best out from the two techniques and to hide their weakness.

4.3.1 Object Declaration Mechanism(OD)

Object declaration (OD) is a server side technique to pass the information about embedded object usage in a web page to a client as early as possible, hopefully at the arrival of the first or second data chunk of its container object instead of waiting for the later chunks. Here, it tries to decouple the description of information about embedded object usage from their actual use. Once this is done, some kind of "pre-loading" can take place to accelerate web page retrieval.

To achieve this goal, we would like to borrow the concept of variable declaration from programming languages. Variable declaration is a common feature in most programming languages such as C and Pascal. Before a variable is used, it needs to be declared in the beginning of a program or a procedure/function routine. This is to help the program in resource allocation and compiler optimization.

To achieve similar effect of variable declaration in web page retrieval, we propose an *optional* declaration of embedded object usage in the beginning of a web page container object. This can be in the form of some new meta-data or a new tag OBJECT_DECLARATION for HTML:

```
<OBJECT_DECLARATION>
ObjectUsageAddr = "URL1"
ObjectUsageAddr = "URL2"
:
```

ObjectUsageAddr = "URL_i"

⋮

ObjectUsageAddr = "URL_n"
</OBJECT_DECLARATION>

where URL_i is the URL address of an embedded object i used in a web page with N distinct embedded objects, $URL_i \neq URL_j$, $1 \leqslant i,\ j \leqslant n$, and $n \leqslant N$. By placing this tag in the beginning of the page container object body, the push-forward effect can be achieved very easily. Note that it is possible for the number of embedded objects declared to be fewer than that actually occurred in a web page because the declaration is only used to assist in performance improvement, but not to ensure accuracy.

After a client receives the first data chunk of a page container object and interprets it, the usage of embedded objects in the page can be found. Earlier object fetching, hopefully in the parallel manner, will then be triggered to speed web page retrieval. In the chunk-level latency dependence graph, this means that the connection of the request object node of an embedded object will be redirected from some original data chunk node of the page container object defining it to the first data chunk node. Using the example in Fig. 4.1 (b), Fig. 4.2 shows the effect of such redirection with object declaration for Obj_B. Note that the retrieval for Obj_B is now pushed forward by the time gap defined by Chk_1 and Chk_4 in the C-LDG.

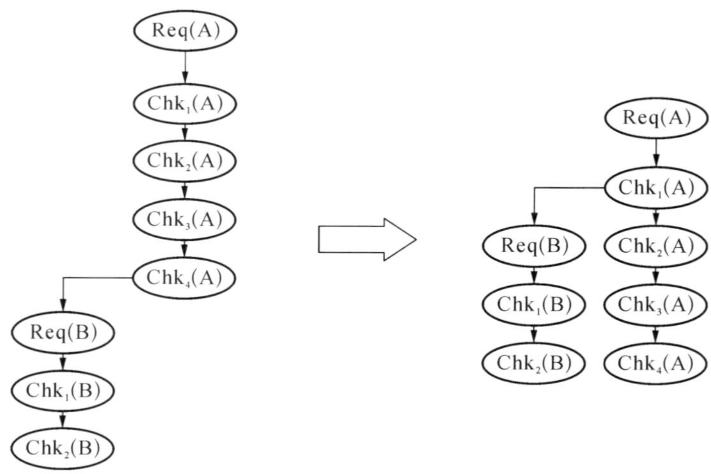

Fig. 4.2 Illustration of push-forward effect of object declaration for Obj_B in C-LDG

To analyze the performance gain of page retrieval using this OD mechanism, let us assume a given web page with N distinct embedded objects Obj_1, Obj_2, ⋯, Obj_i, ⋯, Obj_N and their associated definition time[1] $DT(Obj_i)$, $1 \leqslant i \leqslant N$. The **definition time** $DT(Obj_i)$ of an embedded object Obj_i is defined as the time gap between the time of

[1] Note that the term "definition time" here is the same as what is defined in Chapter 3.

sending out the request for the page container object Pri_Obj_c to the arrival time of the data chunk Chk_j of Pri_Obj_c that defines the first time use of Obj_i in the page. We further assume that the arrival time of the first data chunk of Pri_Obj_c is RT and there is only one level of object embedding in the page for the sake of easy discussion.

First, we know that the following relationships are true:

- $RT \leqslant DT(Obj_1)$
- $DT(Obj_i) \leqslant DT(Obj_{i+1})$ for $\forall\, i$: $1 \leqslant i \leqslant N-1$

assuming the definition order of embedded objects in the page follows the value of i. With the OD mechansim, the new definition time of embedded objects $DT'(Obj_i)$ will be reduced as

- $DT'(Obj_i) = RT \leqslant DT(Obj_i)$ for $\forall\, i$: $1 \leqslant i \leqslant N$

Here we assume that the object declaration is in the first returning data chunk of Pri_Obj_c. In practice, it might be in the second data chunk (or even the third chunk) instead because the first chunk is usually reserved for the header field, and the chunk size is non-deterministic. However, this will not affect the validity of our discussion.

In the presence of proxy caching, the following situations will happen:

- If Pri_Obj_c is found in the proxy cache and is still fresh (i.e. a cache hit and life time less than object expire time):
  - $DT'(Obj_i) = DT(Obj_i) = 0$ for $\forall\, i$: $1 \leqslant i \leqslant N$
  - No improvement is obtained, as the information about embedded object usage in the requested page can be found in negligible time, independent of the use of OD mechanism.
- If Pri_Obj_c is not found in the proxy cache (i.e. a cache miss) or it is found in the proxy cache but its life time is expired:
  - $DT'(Obj_i) = RT \leqslant DT(Obj_i)$ for $\forall\, i$: $1 \leqslant i \leqslant N$
  - This situation happens when either:
    - The fresh content of Pri_Obj_c is retrieved from the web server and the embedded object usage of the page is specified in the first data chunk of Pri_Obj_c.
    - The current content of Pri_Obj_c is re-validated without the actual data transfer, and the first chunk of the replied data allows the extraction of the embedded object usage information from the local cached copy of Pri_Obj_c in negligible time.
  - Improvement in retrieval latency can potentially be obtained with the help of parallel object fetching.

From the above discussion, we see that the OD mechanism reduces the retrieval latency of embedded objects in a web page through the earlier availability of their usage information in Pri_Obj_c. There is one limitation that the mechanism can not go beyond. The new definition time $DT'(Obj_i)$ for each embedded object in the requested page (in the case of an object cache miss) is non-zero. Of course, what this means to the actual web page latency depends on both the parallelism width and the theoretical upper bound speedup. Note that the upper bound speedup of web page retrieval through "push-forward" effect is defined as the maximum of retrieval time of any embedded object in the page in the presence of infinite parallelism width.

It is worth mentioning here that there is an important difference between the variable declaration in a program and the object declaration in a web page. The former one, variable declaration, is to ensure program accuracy. Hence, the requirement is very strict; all variables need to be declared before they can be used else errors will occur. The object declaration, however, mainly serves as hints to improve web page retrieval. No error is expected even if some embedded objects in the page are not declared or the client does not understand the meta-data or new tag used in the OD mechanism.

4.3.2 History-Based Page Structure Table Mechanism (PST)

History-based page structure table mechanism (PST) is an alternate client-side mechanism to achieve similar push-forward effect of reducing page retrieval latency as the OD mechanism does. One basic requirement of the OD mechanism is the collaboration with the content providers to include hints of object usage in web pages, which might sometimes be difficult to obtain. Its push-forward effect on the definition time of embedded objects is also limited to the time of getting the first data chunk of the page container object.

To address these two issues, we propose a page structure table (PST) to record the information about embedded object usage of web pages through their previous reference history. This PST can be viewed as a separate mapping table similar to the proxy cache index table and it is implemented either in the client browser or the forward proxy cache. Each entry in the table contains the URL of the page container object Pri_Obj_c and its associated expire time, together with the URLs of the distinct embedded objects used in the page. Figure 4.3 shows the typical entry of a PST. The URL of Pri_Obj_c is used as the index to the table. Its expire time indicates the validity of the current object usage record. It is set exactly to be the same as the expire time field in the HTTP transfer header of Pri_Obj_c. The rationale behind this rule is that the life-times of the data content and the embedded object usage information of Pri_Obj_c should be the same. The ObjectUsageAddr field gives the URL of the embedded object used in Pri_Obj_c.

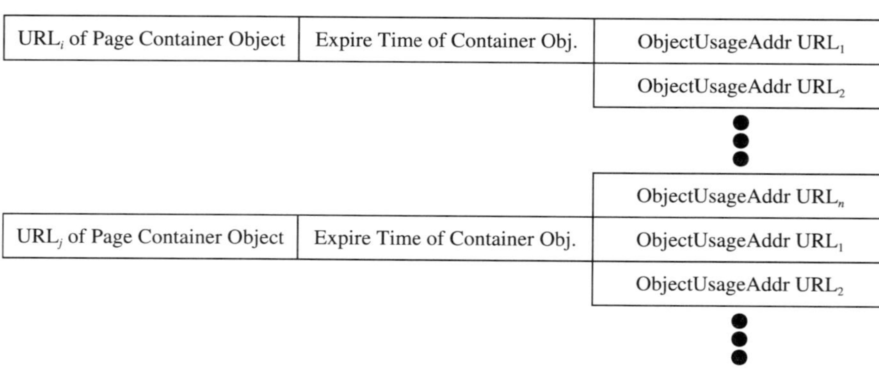

Fig. 4.3 Entry of page structure table

When a web page is requested, the URL of Pri_Obj_c is checked against the PST. Advanced pre-loading of embedded objects in the page and field updating of the table entries will be done according to the following rules:

(1) If there is a hit in the PST and the expire time of Pri_Obj_c is not exceeded, the information about the embedded object usage in the page will be retrieved for early parallel object fetching.

(2) If there is a hit in the PST but the expire time of Pri_Obj_c has already passed, the content of Pri_Obj_c will be fetched and analyzed. The information about the embedded object usage in the page will be extracted and be used to update the corresponding fields of the Pri_Obj_c's entry in the PST. The expire time field of the entry will also be updated.

(3) If there is a cache miss in the PST, a slot entry will be allocated in the PST with the URL of Pri_Obj_c as the index. Both the object usage fields and the expire time field of the entry will be updated as in case (2) above.

In both case (2) and (3), the updating of the PST will be done when Pri_Obj_c is written into the proxy cache. As a result, the new information will benefit the future reuse of the page, not the current access.

The size of the PST is expected to be much smaller than that of the proxy cache because it only contains the object usage information of the page and not the actual data content inside. In terms of the space management of the PST, there are two situations that we need to consider.

The first one is the overflow of the embedded object usage space per entry. This is due to the theoretical large number of embedded objects used in a web page. To handle this situation, the URLs of the embedded objects with large object sizes and appearing towards the end of Pri_Obj_c should be given high priorities because this will give better cost-effective use of the table space. The URLs of those embedded objects that can not be entered into the slot can simply be dropped because this will not affect the accuracy of web page retrieval. Due to the very high performance of the PST and its relatively small size, one practical implementation for the management of the ObjectUsageAddr fields in a PST row is to use the first-in-first-out mechanism.

The second situation is the overflow of the PST entries. Here, we recommend its replacement policy to be the same as that of its proxy cache such as LRU, LFU and Greedy-Dual (Cao and Irani 1997). This decision is based on the assumption that its reuse pattern is quite similar to that in the proxy cache.

Based on the working mechanism described above, we see that the history-based PST mechanism functions slightly different from the OD mechanism. For the first time access of a web page (or access to a page with new life time period), the PST mechanism does not offer any reduction in the page retrieval latency. This is because no information about the usage information about embedded objects for the request page can be found in the table. However, when a page is reused and its Pri_Obj_c is missed from the cache, ideal reduction of having zero definition time for its embedded object retrieval is obtained. This is shown by the chunk-level latency dependence graph in

Fig. 4.4, where the push-forward effect of Obj_B brings forward its request node to the request node of Pri_Obj_c instead of the first data chunk Chk_1 of Pri_Obj_c.

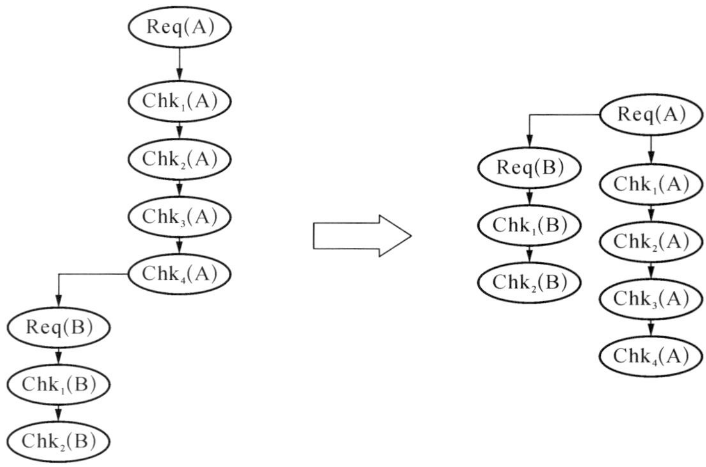

Fig. 4.4 Illustration of push-forward effect of history-based PST mechanism

To understand the performance gain of page retrieval using the history-based PST mechanism, we continue our discussion of performance gain in the last section. Based on the similar notations and assumptions, we see that in the presence of proxy cache and the PST, the new definition time of embedded objects $DT''(Obj_i)$ for a page request will be reduced as:

- If Pri_Obj_c is found in the proxy cache:
  - The expire time of Pri_Obj_c in the PST must be equal to that in the proxy cache.
  - If Pri_Obj_c is still fresh (i.e. its life time $\leqslant$ expire time in proxy):
    - $DT''(Obj_i) = DT(Obj_i) = 0$ for $\forall\, i\colon 1 \leqslant i \leqslant N$
    - No improvement is obtained, as the information about the usage of embedded objects in the requested page can be found in negligible time, either from the PST or from the local cached copy of Pri_Obj_c.
  - If Pri_Obj_c in the proxy cache needs revalidation but without actual content transfer:
    - $DT''(Obj_i) = DT(Obj_i) = RT$ for $\forall\, i\colon 1 \leqslant i \leqslant N$
    - No improvement is obtained, as the information about the embedded object usage can be found in the local cached copy of Pri_Obj_c after one round trip of short message validation between the server and the client. Note that the expire time of Pri_Obj_c in the PST must not be larger than that in the proxy cache.
  - If Pri_Obj_c in the proxy cache needs revalidation and causes actual data transfer, or if Pri_Obj_c in the proxy cache is invalid and needs the actual data transfer from the web server:

        - $DT''(Obj_i) = DT(Obj_i)$ for $\forall\ i:\ 1 \leqslant i \leqslant N$
        - No improvement in the page retrieval latency is expected, as the information about the embedded object usage in the requested page needs to be extracted from Pri_Obj_c that is being streamed from the web server to the client. In this case, intra-page rescheduling can be done.
    - In all these cases, we see that the history-based PST can not give any page latency reduction if a copy of Pri_Obj_c is found in the proxy cache. Furthermore, this conclusion is independent of the freshness of Pri_Obj_c and the content in the PST.
- If Pri_Obj_c is missed from the proxy cache:
    - If the expire time of Pri_Obj_c in the PST is not exceeded:
        - $DT''(Obj_i) = 0 \leqslant DT(Obj_i)$ for $\forall\ i:\ 1 \leqslant i \leqslant N$
        - Improvement in the page retrieval latency is expected, as the information about the embedded object usage of the requested page in the PST can be used to accelerate the actual page retrieval. In this case, the definition times for all the embedded objects in the page are equal to zero.
    - If the expire time of the container object in the PST has passed:
        - $DT''(Obj_i) = DT(Obj_i)$ for $\forall\ i:\ 1 \leqslant i \leqslant N$
        - No improvement in the page retrieval latency is expected, as the information about the embedded object usage of the requested page in the PST is invalid. Any prefetching of embedded objects based on this information might result in unnecessary traffic[1] (but not the accuracy).

From the above discussion, we see that the history-based PST mechanism works in the situation of reuse of web pages with their container page object not found in the proxy cache. Hence, its performance will be related to the reuse pattern of the web references.

4.3.3 Analysis of Object Declaration and History-Based PST Mechanisms

In the last two sub-sections, we purposed two mechanisms to achieve the push-forward effect for intra-page rescheduling of web pages. Comparing the two mechanisms, we see that each has its pros and cons.

The OD mechanism is theoretically simpler to implement because each page container object only needs to declare its embedded object usage, just like the variable declaration in programming languages. In this aspect, the PST mechanism is relatively more complex because it needs to manage the history table.

In terms of the performance, the OD approach is expected to have better average performance than the PST one. This argument is based on the observation that about two

---

[1] Note that in actual practice, parallel object fetching based on the invalid information of embedded object usage in a page might still give performance improvement because many "dynamic" web objects only change a relatively small segment(e.g. advertisement banner) of the objects and their embedded object usages are still very similar to the previous versions.

thirds of the web pages are found not to be reused in typical proxy caches. While the OD mechanism can work on any situation, the PST works only on the situation of page reuse with its container object not found in the proxy cache.

However, the OD mechanism also has its drawbacks. The most important one is the collaboration with the content providers. In order for the mechanism to work, the container object needs to be modified to include the new tag or meta-data. Also, the OD mechanism can not completely eliminate the definition times of embedded objects under all situations while the PST mechanism can sometimes do it for the subsequent access to the same page that is missed from the proxy cache.

One common concern of these two approaches is the information size of the embedded object usage in a web page. In theory, the number of distinct embedded objects used in a web page can be very big. This might in turn cause substantial increase in the size of the container object page for the OD mechanism and overflow in the object usage fields of the history table for the PST mechanism.

While this concern is valid, we argue that we only need to declare *enough* embedded objects to use up the parallelism width during the retrieval time of the page container object. So long as it can keep the fetching pipes busy, there is no need to do a full version. This is important because it will put an upper bound to the number of objects that need to be declared (or hinted) and in turn the size increase of the page container object. Based on this argument and the current popular parallelism width of four, we find that the information size of the embedded object usage needed per page container object is very small. The rule of thumb for the number of distinct embedded object URLs needed to be book-kept is about twice the parallelism width for simultaneous object fetching. One important thing that needs to be pointed out here is that in the case of very large page container object with lots of embedded objects inside, it is true that the fetching pipes might not be fully packed. However, what will be lost here is just some performance in some extreme, rarely occurred cases, but the accuracy of the page retrieval is not affected.

Finally, we see that the two mechanisms can actually work together to enhance the effect of each other. The object declaration mechanism can be used as the basic mechanism to achieve the push-forward effect for accelerating web page request. Whenever a web page is reused and is not found in the proxy cache, the PST mechanism can further reduces the definition times of its embedded objects to zero by making use of the information in the PST.

4.4 Experimental Study

To illustrate the potentials of our push-forward mechanisms, trace driven simulation on proxy caching is conducted. Details about our simulation environment can be summarized as follows: Three proxy traces i.e. Berkeley, Digital, and NLANR are taken from the Internet Traffic Archive (http://ita.ee.lbl.gov/index.html), the most commonly used trace repository for web caching research community. Each trace contains at least 1.5 millions object references. For the simulator, three commonly used replacement algorithms, LRU, LFU, and Greedy-Dual (GDS) (Cao and Irani 1997) are studied. The simulated cache size varies from 5%, 10%, 15%, and 20% of the total size of unique objects recorded in the traces. Parallelism width for simultaneous object fetching also ranges from 4, 8, 16, to 32. The proxy cache without push-forward mechanisms is used as the reference for comparison. The object declaration OD, history-based PST, and a combination of both OD_PST are simulated to find out their relative potentials. In the sensitivity study, a proxy cache size of 10% of total distinct object sizes in the trace and a parallelism width of four are used as the standard configuration and the parameter under study is varied to find out its impact on proxy cache performance.

The primary measurement parameter of our study is the page retrieval latency, which is defined as the time of sending out an URL page request to the receiving of the last chunk of data from objects belonging to the page. Each trace is preprocessed to estimate the definition time DT of each object retrieval for a page request, relative to the starting of the page request. However, due to the granularity of the trace data and the implicit parallelism width of four simultaneous objects fetching, some assumptions about the definition times of embedded objects in a page request need to be made for the trace data. For a page request, what can be observed can be summarized as

- DT (page container object) = 0.
- DT (ith embedded object) $\leqslant$ observed time gap between the container object request and the ith embedded object request in the trace, where $1 \leqslant i \leqslant 3$.
- DT (3rd embedded object) $\leqslant$ DT (ith embedded object) $\leqslant$ observed time gap between the container object request and the ith embedded object request in the trace, where $i \geqslant 4$.

To ensure the consistency and correctness of our simulation studies, we make the following reasonable, conservative assumption about the definition times of embedded objects:

- DT (page container object) = 0.
- DT (ith embedded object) = observed time gap between the container object request and the ith embedded object request in the trace, where $1 \leqslant i \leqslant 3$.
- DT (ith embedded object) = DT (3rd embedded object), where $i \geqslant 4$.

The assumption is based on the maximum parallelism width of four for simultaneous object fetching in current browsers and is reflected in the trace data. Note that in order to obtain the exact chunk retrieval time and their latency dependence information, the proxy traces with multi-million entries need to be re-run again and the content of each page container object inside also needs to be parsed. This is not only too time consuming but also impossible because some of the web objects do not exist anymore. Also, the consistency among multiple runs of experiments will be difficult to be ensured in this case.

4.4.1 Potentials of Push-Forward and Parallelism Effect in Web Page Retrieval

The first set of experiments that we would like to conduct is to find out the potentials of the push-forward mechanisms as well as its theoretical performance bound. Figure 4.5 shows the distribution of number of objects per page. This distribution study is important because both the push-forward mechanisms (including object declaration and PST mechanisms) and the adjustment of parallelism width only work for pages with multiple objects. The larger the number of objects per page is, the larger the potentials of these mechanisms will be.

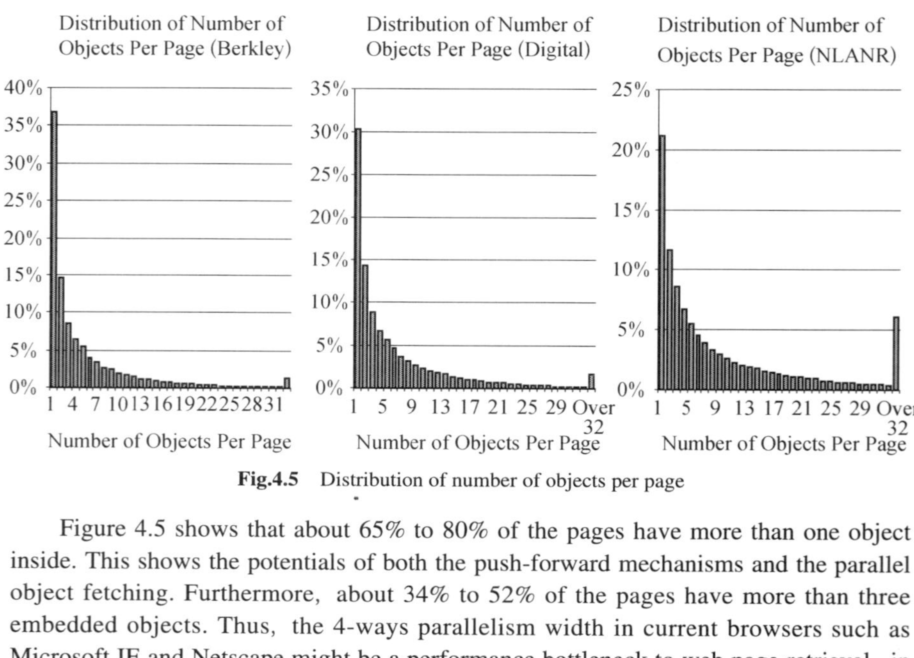

Fig.4.5 Distribution of number of objects per page

Figure 4.5 shows that about 65% to 80% of the pages have more than one object inside. This shows the potentials of both the push-forward mechanisms and the parallel object fetching. Furthermore, about 34% to 52% of the pages have more than three embedded objects. Thus, the 4-ways parallelism width in current browsers such as Microsoft IE and Netscape might be a performance bottleneck to web page retrieval, in particular if the information about the object usage in a page can be made known to the client earlier than the actual object uses.

Figure 4.6 shows the theoretical upper bound reduction of web page retrieval latency with ideal definition times for its embedded objects (i.e. DT (embedded objects) = 0) and infinite parallelism width for simultaneous object fetching. Its value is given by

$$1-\frac{Maximum\,(Retrieval\_Latency\_of\_Object\_in\_Page)}{Overall\_Page\_Retrieval\_Latency}$$

The formula shows that the theoretical upper bound reduction of web page retrieval latency is solely determined by the longest retrieval latency of anyone object (not necessary the embedded ones) in a page. This is reasonable because all the rescheduling mechanisms (including push-forward and parallel fetching) only work on the object level. They can not shorten the retrieval latency of a web object. This information is important because by comparing it with the performance obtained from any rescheduling mechanism, we can find out how much the rescheduling mechanism can be fine-tuned potentially.

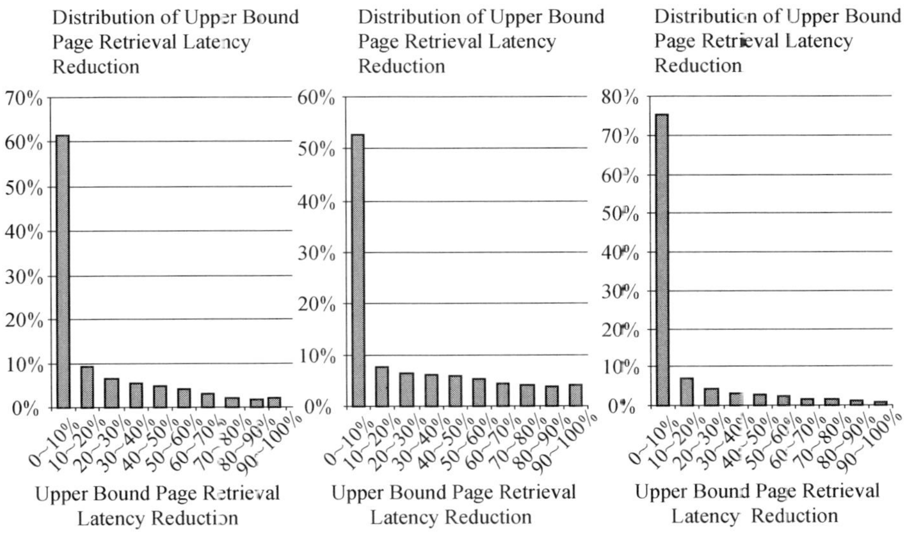

Fig.4.6 Upper bound reduction of page retrieval latency with ideal definition times for embedded objects and infinite parallelism width

The x axis of the graph in Fig.4.6 shows the upper bound reduction of page latency and the y axis shows its distribution percentage. From Fig.4.6, we see that about 53% to 75% of the web pages are expected to have an upper bound page latency reduction of less than 10%. Such a high percentage occurs mostly because there are about 20% to 35% of the pages with single object (refer to Fig.4.5) and they can not be improved by any rescheduling mechanism. For the rest 25% to 47% of the web pages, reasonable performance gain can potentially be obtained. The distribution percentage of pages drops with increasing values of upper bound page latency reduction. This agrees with the distribution of the number of objects per page given in Fig.4.5.

Figure 4.7 repeats the experiments in Fig.4.6 except that the parallelism width is now limited to four, the constraint in today's common browsers. The upper bound reduction of page retrieval latency in this case is given by

$$1-\frac{Page\_Latency\_With\_DT\_of\_Embedded\_Objects = 0\_and\_Parallelism\_Width = 4}{Original\_Page\_Retrieval\_Latency\_With\_Parallelism\_Width = 4}$$

We see that all the three distribution curves shift to the left by 10% and their shapes remain the same. This gives us some idea about the importance of parallel object fetching to page retrieval latency once the problem about the definition time of embedded objects in the page is resolved.

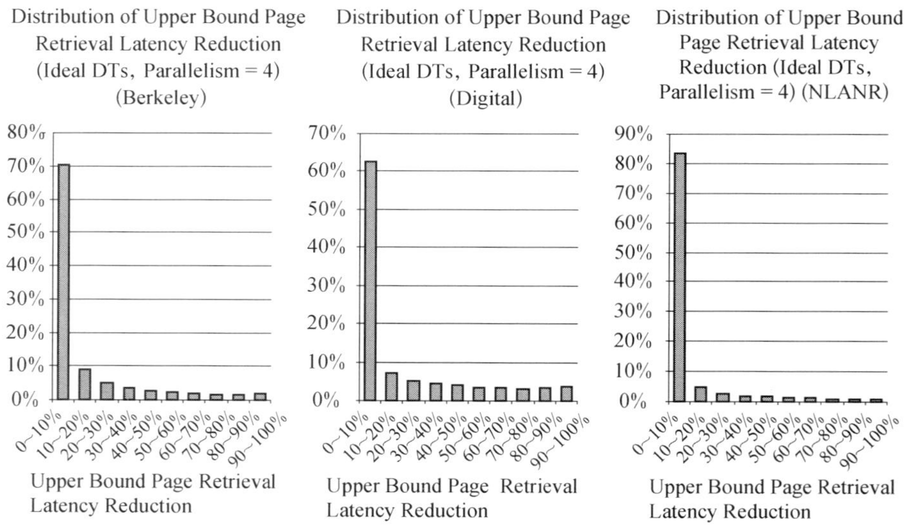

Fig.4.7 Upper bound reduction of page retrieval latency with ideal definition times for embedded objects(DTs = 0) and parallelism width = 4

4.4.2 Effect of Object Declaration Mechanism

To understand the potentials of the OD mechanism, we would like to first find out the realistic upper bound latency reduction of page retrieval, subject to the constraints of the mechanism and the parallelism width of four.

The push-forward effect of the OD mechanism is supposed to make the definition times of the embedded objects to be the retrieval time of the first or second data chuck of the page container object. As a lower estimate for the upper bound latency reduction by the mechanism, it will be interesting to find out the performance impact when the definition time of the ith embedded object $DT(Obj_i)$ is set to be equal to the definition time of the 1st embedded object $DT(Obj_1)$. Figure 4.8 repeats the experiments of Fig.4.6 with this approximation made to the definition times of embedded objects. The realistic upper bound reduction of page retrieval latency by the OD mechanism is given by

$$1-\frac{Page\_Latency\_With\_DT(Obj_i) = DT(Obj_i)\ \_and\_Parallelism\_Width = 4}{Original\_Page\_Retrieval\_Latency\_With\_Parallelism\_Width = 4}$$

As is expected, the non-ideal definition times for the embedded objects in page retrieval shift all the three performance curves in Fig.4.7 again to the left by about 10% to 20%. With this performance graph, we should expect the realistic performance gain by the OD mechanism to be about 5% to 10%, assuming no change to the parallelism width. This is already quite significant, taking into consideration of the simplicity of the OD mechanism.

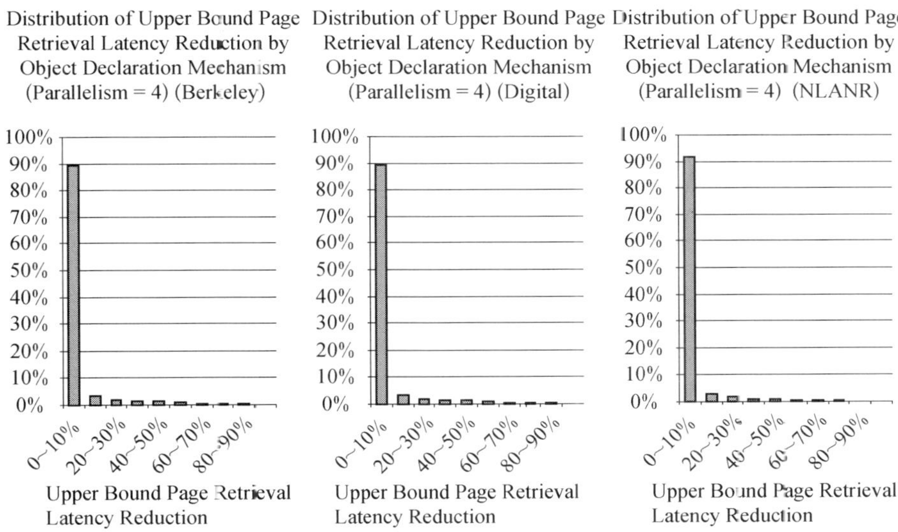

Fig.4.8 Upper bound reduction of page retrieval latency by OD mechanism, with embedded objects' $DT(Obj_i) = DT(Obj_1)$ and parallelism width = 4

Next, we would like to find out the actual performance gain of the OD mechanism when it is implemented in the proxy cache environment. The result is shown in Fig.4.9. In Fig.4.9, the x axis is the proxy cache size, defined in terms of the percentage of total unique objects size in the trace. The y axis is the normalized page retrieval latency reduction by the X push-forward mechanism, which is defined by the following formula:

$$1-\frac{\sum Page\_Latency\_With\_X\_Push\text{-}Forward\_Mechanism\_and\_Proxy\_Cache}{\sum Original\_Page\_Latency\_Without\_X\_Mechanism\_but\_With\_Same\_Proxy\_Cache}$$

The result in Fig.4.9 is very encouraging, as the normalized overall page retrieval latency can be reduced by 3% to 12%, which is very significant. Compared to LRU and LFU, the normalized latency reduction gain in GDS is the largest. This observation is not difficult to explain. GDS is generally considered to be the most efficient algorithm among these three replacement policies. Since its policy takes the page structure into consideration, their latency reduction is the result of predicting reusable pages more than sharing of frequently used objects. For LRU and LFU, the caching emphasis on the frequently used objects reduces the average number of embedded objects retrieved (in the form of cache misses) per page. This causes the normalized latency reduction gain by LRU and LFU to be lower than that by GDS.

The argument about the performance difference among the three replacement policies is further supported by what happens to the normalized latency reduction gain with increasing cache size. For GDS, the normalized latency reduction gain is quite

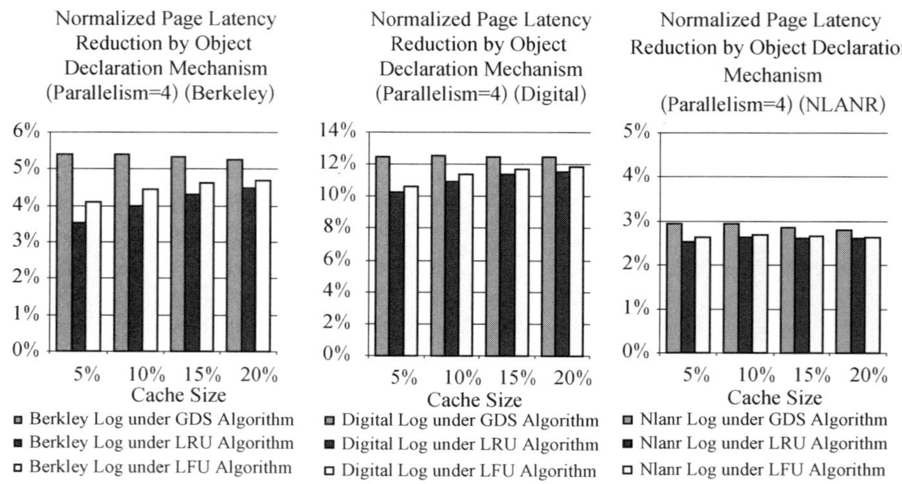

Fig.4.9 Normalized overall page retrieval latency reduction by OD mechanism and parallelism width = 4

constant, being insensitive to the change of cache size. This is due to its consideration of multiple characteristics of an object for caching. However, for LRU and LFU, the normalized gain increases with cache size. A larger cache size implies more page container objects to be reused. Thus, the "visible" sharing effect on the number of missing embedded objects per page mentioned above is reduced and the normalized latency reduction gain increases with cache size. Note that Fig.4.9 shows the values of the normalized page retrieval latency reduction gain but not their absolute ones; the absolute value of latency reduction gain increases with increasing cache size, independent of the replacement policies and the traces.

Figure 4.9 also shows that there is difference in the normalized latency reduction gains from the three traces, with Digital the largest and NLANR the least. While the difference in the characteristics of page composition definitely exists among the traces, detailed investigation reveals another explanation to this observation. This is due to the frequent use of javascripts in the NLANR trace. In this set of experiments, we push forward the definition times of all embedded objects to the definition time of the first embedded object and assume that the definition time of the first embedded object is equal to the retrieval time of the first data chunk of the page container object. While this assumption is valid to most HTMLs, it is too conservative for javascripts. This is because javascript needs to be retrieved entirely and parsed before it can trigger the retrieval of the first embedded object inside. In other words, there is a big time gap between the arrival of the first data chunk of a javascript and the definition time of its first embedded object.

Finally, we would like to find out the impact of the parallelism width on the performance of the OD mechanism. In particular, it is interesting to find out if the push-forward effect can be fully utilized by the increased parallelism width for simultaneous object fetching.

The result is shown in Fig.4.10. The x axis is the parallelism width for simultaneous object fetching and the y axis is the normalized page latency reduction by the OD mechanism. It shows that the two effects indeed multiply each other, independent of the traces and the replacement policies. As the parallelism width increases, the OD mechanism becomes more effective. The curve for the normalized page latency reduction starts to level off at the parallelism width of 16. This is expected because the absolute latency reduction curve against the parallelism width is also leveled off at this parallelism width. Hence, we show that with sufficient retrieval parallelism, more embedded objects can be fetched earlier with the advanced information about the usage of embedded objects in a page. Note that although the normalized page latency reduction does not increase dramatically with the parallelism width, its absolute value is indeed the case.

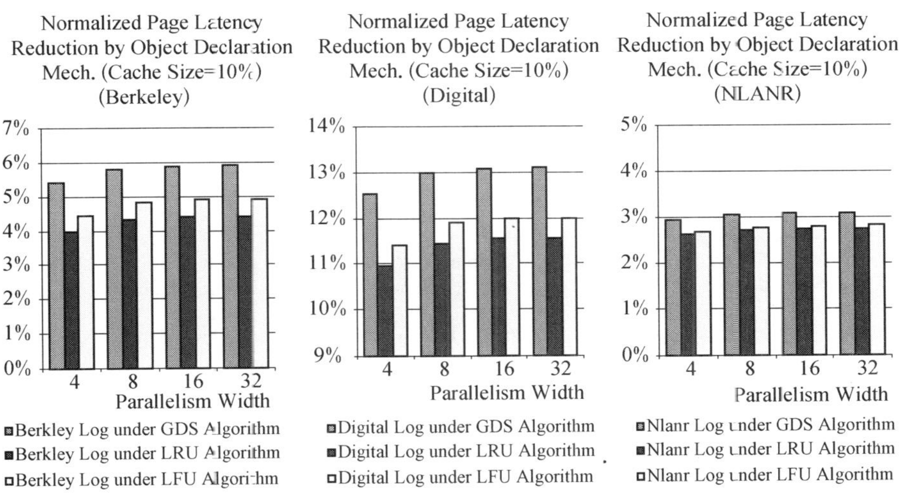

Fig.4.10 Normalized overall page retrieval latency reduction by OD mechanism and cache size = 10% of total unique objects size

4.4.3 Effect of History-Based Page Structure Table (PST) Mechanism

In this section, we would like to find out the potentials of the PST mechanism on the reduction of the page retrieval latency. Similar sets of experiments are conducted as those for the OD mechanism in Section 4.4.2.

First, we would like to find out the realistic upper bound latency reduction of page retrieval, subject to the constraints of the PST mechanism and the 4-way parallelism width. In the ideal situation, the push-forward effect of the PST mechanism is supposed to make the definition times of all embedded objects in page retrieval to zero if the page is referenced again for the ith times, where $i \geqslant 2$.

Figure 4.11 shows the distribution of the upper bound page latency reduction by the PST mechanism. The x axis is still the percentage reduction in the upper bound page latency and the y axis is its percentage distribution. Once again, we observe that about 90% of the web pages are expected to have an upper bound latency reduction of about 10%. By comparing it with the corresponding graph for the OD mechanism (in Fig.4.8), we see that the two distributions are very similar, both in their shapes and values. Hence, the realistic performance gain by the PST mechanism should be about 5% to 10%.

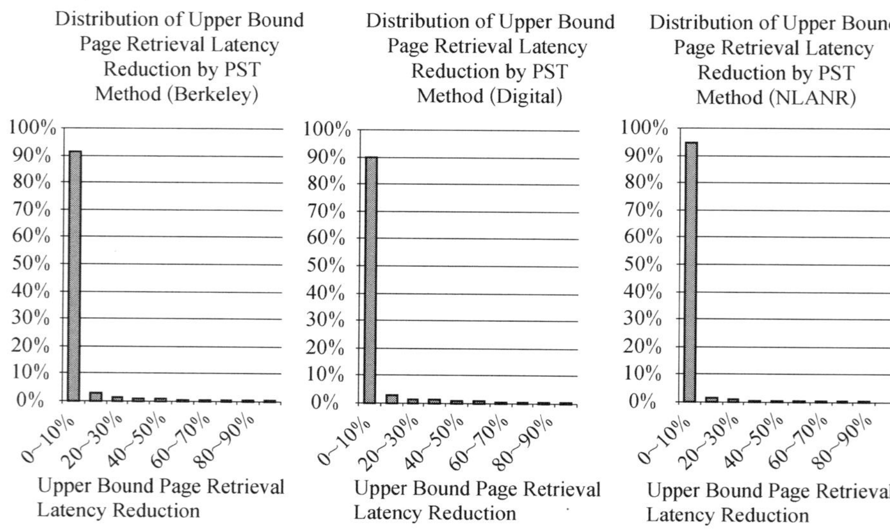

Fig. 4.11 Upper bound reduction of page retrieval latency by PST mechanism, with embedded objects' DT(Obj_i) = 0 for all reused pages and parallelism width = 4

Although the upper bound latency reduction gains of the PST and OD mechanisms are very similar, their performances in the presence of proxy cache are very different. Figure 4.12 shows the normalized page latency reduction by the PST mechanism.

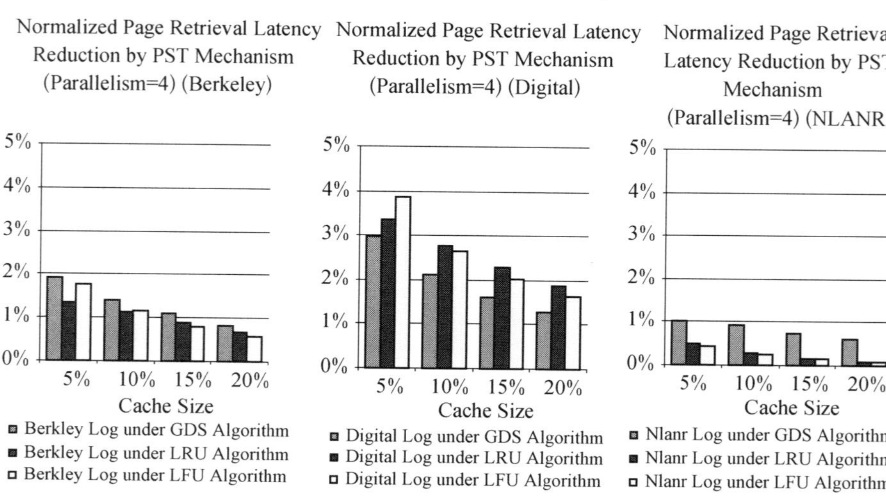

Fig.4. 12 Normalized overall page retrieval latency reduction by PST mechanism and parallelism width = 4

The x axis is still the cache size (in terms of the total unique objects size) and the y axis is the normalized page latency reduction. Rather than the expected 5% to 10% performance improvement (as compared to Fig.4.9 for the OD case), only 1% to 4% of the latency reduction can be observed for the three replacement policies among all the traces. Further investigation on this surprising result shows that this is due to the difference in their source for performance contribution. For the OD mechanism, the source comes from pages retrieved from the original web servers. The presence of the proxy cache does not significantly affect the way a page (with its container object and multiple embedded objects) is retrieved. However, for the PST mechanism, the situation is very different. Since its performance source mainly comes from those reused web pages, the presence of proxy cache will take away its chance for performance, thus resulting in a much lower normalized page latency reduction.

This argument is further supported by what happens to the normalized page latency reduction with increasing cache size. The normalized latency reduction actually drops with increasing cache size, an opposite phenomenon to what we observe for the OD mechanism in Fig.4 9. This supports our argument that the better the proxy cache can perform (e.g. by increasing the cache size), the lesser the PST mechanism can contribute to the page latency reduction. Nevertheless, the PST mechanism has its potentials because of the limited performance a proxy cache can provide. Furthermore, a 1% to 3% reduction in page latency is still a non-negligible performance gain, in particular with just a simple PST and no server/client collaboration. One more observation of Fig. 4.12 is that the impact of the PST mechanism to the page latency reduction is quite insensitive to the replacement policies, another difference from the Fig.4.9.

Once again, we want to emphasize that what is shown in Fig.4.12 is the normalized page latency reduction. Although the shape of the curves for all the traces decreases with increasing cache size, this does not mean that their absolute values drop with bigger caches. Here, we just want to focus the contribution of the PST mechanism to a given cache environment.

Just like the last section, we would also like to find out the impact of the parallelism width on the performance of the PST mechanism. The result is shown in Fig.4.13, where the x axis is the parallelism width for simultaneous object fetching and the y axis is the normalized latency reduction by the PST mechanism. It shows that unlike the OD situation (as is shown in Fig.4.10), the multiplying effect of the PST with the parallelism width is not very obvious. This is probably due to the fact that the parallelism width helps the first time page access much more than the reuse of web pages that are missed from the proxy cache.

4.4.4 Effect of Integrated OD and PST Mechanism

In the last two sections, we present detailed analysis of how the two push-forward mechanisms can contribute to the page retrieval latency reduction. We observe that although their potentials are similar, their sources for performance contribution are

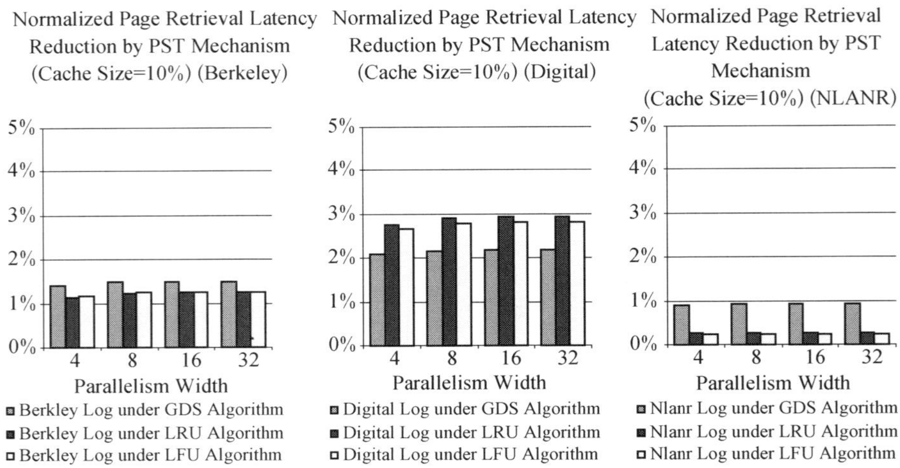

Fig. 4.13 Normalized overall page retrieval latency reduction by PST mechanism and cache size = 10% of total unique objects size

quite different. And this results in the difference in their actual performance in the presence of a proxy cache. Since they are compliment to each other, we would like to find out the potentials if these two mechanisms are used together, which we call it the integrated OD_PST mechanism. Once again, similar sets of experiments are conducted as those found in the last two sections.

Figure 4.14 shows the distribution of the upper bound page retrieval latency reduction by the OD_PST mechanism. The x axis is still the percentage reduction in the upper bound page retrieval latency and the y axis is its percentage distribution. In terms of the potentials, the two mechanisms indeed reinforce each other, thus shifting the performance graphs of the OD and PST mechanisms (Fig.4.8 and Fig.4.11) to the right by about 5% to 10%. By comparing Fig.4.14 with Fig.4.7 (the ideal latency reduction with limited parallelism width of four), we see that this integrated OD_PST mechanism actually has performance that is quite close to the ideal one. With the result in Fig.4.11, we expect the realistic performance gain by the OD_PST mechanism to be about 5% to 20%.

Next, we would like to find out how much this potential of the OD_PST mechanism can be converted into actual performance gain in the presence of the proxy cache. The result is shown in Fig.4.15. The x axis is still the proxy cache size and the y axis is the normalized page retrieval latency reduction by the mechanism. Figure 4.15 shows that with the integrated OD_PST mechanism, the overall normalized page retrieval latency can be reduced by 3% to 18%, which is very significant. This also shows the multiplying effect of the OD and PST mechanisms.

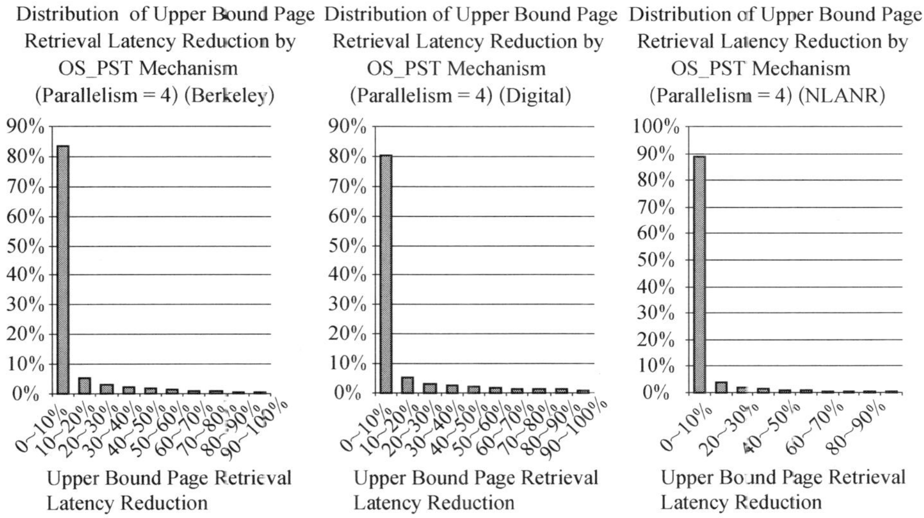

Fig. 4.14 Upper bound reduction of page retrieval latency by OD_PST mechanism and parallelism width = 4

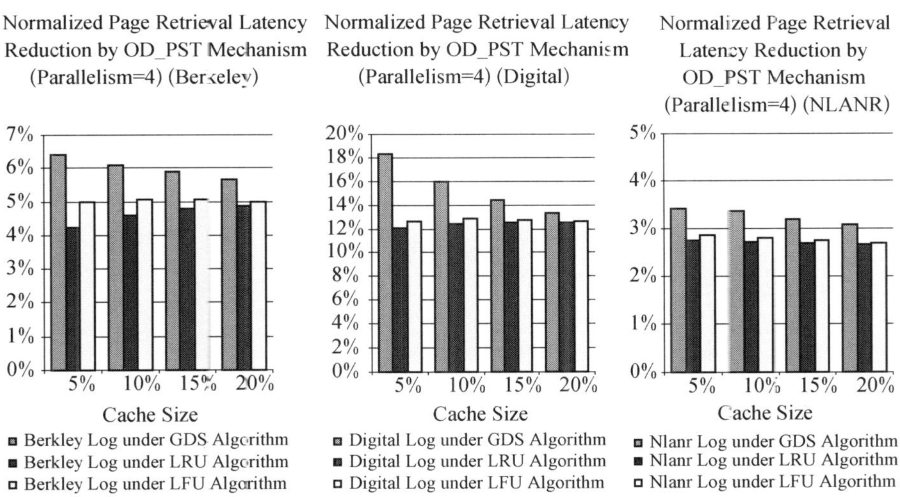

Fig. 4.15 Normalized overall page retrieval latency reduction by OD_PST and parallelism width = 4

Generally speaking, the performance characteristics of the OD_PST and the OD only mechanisms are quite similar with respect to the different parameters such as traces and replacement policies. This is expected because the OD mechanism is supposed to have much stronger dominating effects over the PST ones. However, there is one exception. Under the GDS replacement policy, the normalized page latency reduction decreases with increasing cache size, the phenomenon for the PST mechanism instead of the OD mechanism.

Finally, we would like to complete our study by finding out the performance impact of the parallelism width on the OD_PST mechanism. The result is shown in Fig.4.16. As is expected, the three graphs follow closely those for the OD mechanism (shown in Fig.4.10). The only exception is the expected larger normalized latency reduction as we expected.

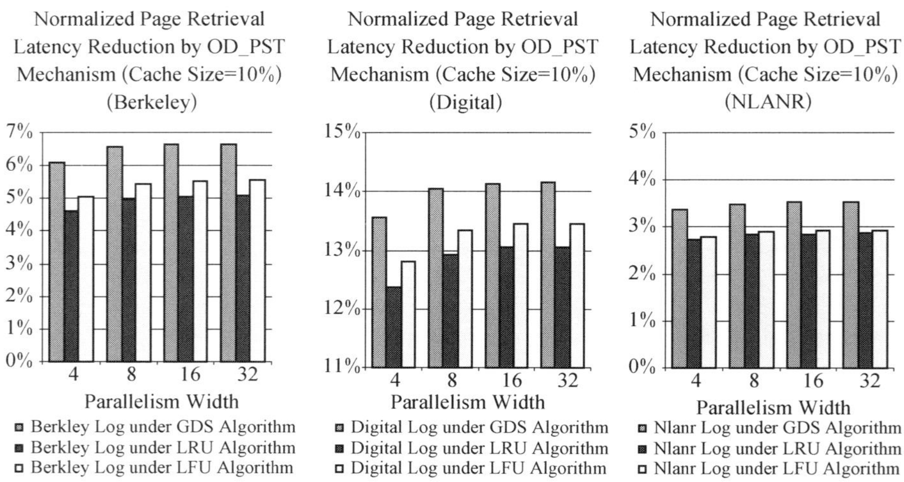

Fig.4.16 Normalized overall page retrieval latency reduction by OD_PST mechanism and cache size = 10% of total unique objects size

Overall speaking, we can see that the OD mechanism and the PST mechanism are complimentary to each other. They work and reinforce each other to provide significant improvement in page retrieval latency reduction, ranging from 3% to 18%.

4.5 Conclusion

In this chapter, we proposed two mechanisms, the object declaration and the page structure table, to achieve the push-forward effect for intra-page rescheduling. While the object declaration mechanism is the server side solution, the PST mechanism is the proxy side implementation. Although they have similar potentials in page retrieval latency reduction, their different sources for performance gain result in their different observed latency reduction percentages in the presence of the proxy cache. Since these two techniques are complimentary to each other, they can work and reinforce each other to give significant latency reduction in web page retrieval, with improvement ranging from a few percents to about 18%.

References

(Cao and Irani 1997) Cao P, Irani S(1997) Cost-Aware WWW WWW Proxy Caching

Algorithms. In: Proceedings of USENIX Symposium on Internet Technologies and Systems, Monterey, CA., USA, December 1997

(Cohen and Kaplan 2000) Cohen E, Kaplan H (2000) Prefetching the Means for Document Transfer: A New Approach for Reducing Web Latency. In: Proceedings of IEEE INFOCOM00, Tel-Aviv, Israel, 2000

(Duchamp 1999) Duchamp D (1999) Prefetching Hyperlinks. In: Proceedings of USENIX Symposium on Internet Technologies and Systems, Boulder, Colorado, USA, October 1999

(EXPAN 2010) Expand Networks (2010) http: //www.expand.com. Accessed 14 April 2010

(Fox and Brewer 1996) Fox A, Brewer E A (1996) Reducing WWW Latency and Bandwidth Requirements via Real-Time Distillation. In: Proceedings of the 5th International World Wide Web Conference (WWW-5), Paris, France, May 1996

(Fox et al. 1998) Fox A, Gribble S D, Chawathe Y et al (1998) Adapting to Network and Client Variation Using Active Proxies: Lessons and perspectives. IEEE Personal Communications 5: 10-19

(Glassman 1994) Glassman S (1994) A Caching Relay for the World-Wide Web. In: Proceedings of 1st International World-Wide Web Conference, CERN, Geneva, Switzerland, May 1994

(Han et al. 1998) Han R, Bhagwat P, LaMaire R et al (1998) Dynamic Adaptation In an Image Transcoding Proxy For Mobile Web Browsing, IEEE Personal Communications 2: 8-17

(HTTP0 1996) Hypertext Transfer Protocol—HTTP/1.0 (1996) In: RFC. http: // www.w3.org/Protocols/HTTP/1.0/draft-ietf-http-spec. html. Accessed 14 April 2010

(HTTP1 1999) Hypertext Transfer Protocol—HTTP/1.1 (1999) In: RFC. http: //www.w3.org/Protocols/rfc2616/rfc2616.html. Accessed 14 April, 2010

(IRCAC) IRCACHE daily report. http://www.ircache.net/Statistics/Summaries/Root. Accessed 18 April 2010

(Kroeger et al. 1997) Kroeger T M, Long D E, Mogul J C (1997) Exploring the Bounds of Web Latency Reduction from Caching and Prefetching In: Proceedings of USENIX Symposium on Internet Technologies and Systems, Monterey, California, USA, December 1997

(Luotonen and Altis 1994) Luotonen A, Altis K (1994) World Wide Web proxies. Computer Networks and ISDN systems 27 (2): 147-154

(Padmanabhan and Mogul 1996) Padmanabhan V N, Mogul J C (1996) Using Predictive Prefetching to Improve World Wide Web Latency. ACM SIGCOMM Computer Communication Review 26 (3): 22-36

(Wang and Cao 1998) Wang Z, Cao P (1998) Persistent Connections Behavior of Popular Browsers. http: //pages.cs.wisc.edu/~cao/papers/persistent-connection. html. Accessed 18 April 2010

(Wessels 2001) Wessels D (2001) Web Caching. Oreilly & Associates, Sebastopol, CA, USA

(Wills et al. 2001) Wills C E, Mikhailov M, Shang H (2001) N for the Price of 1: Bundling Web Objects for More Efficient Content Delivery. In: Proceedings of the 10th International World Wide Web Conference, Hong Kong, May 2001

5

Modes of Real-Time Content Transformation for Web Intermediaries in Active Network

5.1 Introduction

The exponential growth of Internet usage, together with the universal acceptance of the web interface, has already made the Internet to be an important communication media not only in professional offices but also at homes and in public places. In such a pervasive access environment, there are three basic challenges to quality-based web content delivery. They are: (i) best fit content presentation, (ii) content related management and policies, and (iii) value-added web intermediaries.

The growing popularity of pervasive Internet access results in wide variations in web client's hardware devices, network dynamics, and personal preferences. It was surveyed that in the year 2004, there will be more non-PC devices such as cellular phones and PDAs accessing the web than PCs do (Walser and Hager 2001). These non-PC devices have significant difference in their display and computing capabilities. The network bandwidth availability to a web client also ranges from slow mobile connection, modem links, to high speed leased lines. Even worse, it also fluctuates with the instantaneous network workload. Due to the open, global access of the Internet, the personal preference of web surfers for a web page varies. This includes language coding, security, and tradeoff between data quality and downloading time. With the dynamic, non-deterministic needs of web clients, content providers are facing a big challenge of providing the "best-fit" presentation of web content to clients in a cost-effective way.

Information related management and policies are also another concern to enterprises when the Internet is penetrating into offices. Issues like content filtering and blocking, virus protection, and security are important to the deployment of enterprise's Internet infrastructure and setup. With more information and services (such as on-line stock) available on the Internet, employers are now concerning about the time and bandwidth usage an employee spends on non-work related web surfing such as stock monitoring, Internet radio, and MP3 songs downloading (TRACE 2001).

With the ever-increasing expectation from web clients and the severe competition in the web content delivery market, Internet service providers are actively seeking ways to provide value-added services on top of the basic network connectivity (ISP). Some initial examples include local advertisement insertion, watermarking, security acceleration, and tracking/monitoring. Different from the standalone computing environment, implementing these functions on the web faces the problems of streaming web data, real-time performance with respect to a large number of simultaneous client requests, and platform independence (Fox et al. 1998).

To achieve efficient best-fit pervasive web access, to enforce enterprise's Internet related management and policies, and to provide a "plug-in" platform for value-added services, three approaches are often practiced today. They are browser plug-ins, server intervention and proxy transformation.

Browser plug-ins is the most common way to support network applications. For each type of applications, a plug-in software is installed in the client browser. Many applications already have plug-ins available for popular web browsers. If an application is very common (such as the viewing of JPEG objects), the plug-in might even be a standard feature of the browser. In this case, the client support of a web application will no longer be a concern.

This plug-in approach, however, might not be effective for pervasive web access, Internet related management and policies, and web intermediaries. It is true that transformation of data content to fit the hardware specification (e.g. display) of a client's device can possibly be done after an entire object is retrieved to the browser. But the computing power of the client's device might be a problem. Devices like cellular phones and PDAs are not expected to have high computing powers. More importantly, however, the plug-in approach is inappropriate in many application situations. In case where a client tries to trade off web presentation quality for faster access through transformation, filtering, or transcoding, the plug-in approach fails to work. Enforcement of Internet related management and policies in an organization through browser plug-ins is also a problem because very often, it just implies self-regulatory instead of centralized administrated. Furthermore, this approach is usually used to handle small-size tasks such as virus scanning. To do a reasonably larger size task such as language translation, this approach usually does not perform well. Another limitation of this approach is that it lacks the ability to save network bandwidth.

Server side solutions also exist to support pervasive web access. This is usually done by keeping more than one version of the web information in the server. When a server receives an HTTP request from a client, it will try to select and deliver the most appropriate version of the information to the client. This approach seems reasonable in the sense that since the server supports an application, it should know the application and its clients best. However, this argument might not be completely true for Internet applications. Since the web is aimed to provide global service, it might sometimes be difficult for a server to fully understand the requirements and preferences of its clients. Whether a web server maintains a certain version of the information also depends on the client demand and the effort involved. Unless there is high demand for a particular version of the data, the content provider will certainly not consider adding that version of the information into his web site. The wide diversity of web clients' hardware devices, network availability, and personal preferences further makes this approach even more difficult to be implemented. The reason for this is that there are too many possible versions of the content to be supported. Finally, the enforcement of Internet related information management and policies is difficult and sometimes inappropriate in the server approach because it is often a conflict of interest between the content providers and the enforcement administrators.

A new trend of providing the best-fit pervasive web access, Internet related information management and policies, and web intermediaries is to implement these functions and intelligence in an organization's gateway, namely proxy server. This turns the traditional passive network for connectivity into active network with intelligence for content manipulation and adaptation. Functions like selective content filtering and blocking have already started to migrate from the client browser to the proxy gateway. There are several advantages of this migration of applications into the network.

The first one is the better provisioning of the best-fit web data presentation to clients in the pervasive Internet access environment. This is possible because the proxy understands its clients much more than web servers do. A proxy server sees the full picture of a client's access pattern whereas a web server can only see a small snapshot of it. The behavior and preference of clients under a proxy server is also more homogeneous than those visible to a web server, making the proxy solution for selected web intermediaries to be more cost-effective.

Enforcement of an organization's Internet related management and policies is also much easier. A proxy server is centrally administrated by the organization. By routing all Internet traffic to pass through the transparent proxy server, policy enforcement can take place without the need of employee's collaboration. Furthermore, it is a cost-effective, easily maintainable and upgradeable solution since one copy of the network application in a proxy server can serve all clients under it. It is also an easily deployable solution as there is no need for collaboration from the web content server or web clients.

Due to the cost-effectiveness and appropriateness of migrating selected server and browser functions into the network proxy, there are recent initiatives to define and standardize content transformation proxy platforms for active network, thus allowing web intermediaries to act as "soft-chips" and be plugged into the proxy server with minimal effort. The two most important ones are the I-CAP (Internet Content Adaptation Protocol) (ICAP 2010a) and the OPES (Open Pluggable Edge Services) (OPES 2001) protocols. Despite the possibility of being abused to tamper web content, the protocols are finally supported by the IETF due to its potentials and impact to web content and service provisioning (OPES 2001).

The concept of real-time proxy-based content transformation in active network is fairly new. Basic research topics such as algorithm complexity for streaming data manipulation, multimedia modeling for scalable content delivery with maximum data reuse, and data integrity and validation for transformed data are still open for investigation. Systems and prototypes of active networks or real-time content transformation proxies that are reported in literature are quite limited and they are mostly done in an ad hoc manner. More fundamentally, there is no detail and systematic discussion on how transformation should be applied on the streaming web data and its implications to performance.

Generally speaking, there are two approaches to implementing proxy-centric solutions. The first approach is based on real-time data streaming. Transformation is done on the fly, as the data passes through the proxy. There is no change to the network transmission mode and the client perceived time of objects; the proxy also does not need to buffer or hold the transmitting object data. Though ideal, this approach of proxy transformation is not easy to be applied because any transformation algorithm that requires the previously transmitted data or the future data for computation can not be done in the traditional way.

In the second approach, the proxy retrieves and buffers the whole object first, performs the necessary transformation before it sends the transformed result to the next level of the network. Compared to the data streaming approach, whole object transformation is much more popular because there is practically no restriction to the kind of transformation that can take place in the proxy. Although this approach seems to be simple, performance overhead is the main concern. Data buffering often implies an increase in the perceived time of object retrieval, more disk operations, and the interruption of data pipelining in the network. This will in turn delay the retrieval of other objects that depend on this one for their usage definition.

From literature, no comprehensive study on the feasibility, tradeoff, and performance analysis of the various possible transformation models is found. To facilitate the deployment of value-added applications in an active proxy network, we would like to provide a systematic way of analyzing the performance issue of active network and its web intermediaries in this chapter. First, we describe the basic transformation model for web content adaptation. Then we suggest three possible modes of real-time content transformation based on the streaming properties of web data. They are the byte-streaming mode, chunk-streaming mode and whole-file buffering mode. Their pros and cons with respect to the proxy performance and client perceived page latency would be analyzed with the help of the chunk-level latency dependence model we proposed in Chapter 3. Experimental results on these modes of real-time proxy content transformation are then given to support our argument. By comparing with the chunk-streaming mode, it is found that the whole-file buffering mode not only increases the average perceived time of objects by 22.38% to 64.84%, but it also lengthens the average latency of page retrieval by about 10%.

5.2 Basic Web Content Transformation Model

Before we go into the discussion of the modes of real-time content transformation and its implications to client and proxy performance, it will be helpful to define a precise model for web content transformation. This model should be based on the resource and the input data required for the transformation on streaming web data.

With the assumption that a web object is the basic unit of input to a web intermediary and the data sequence of its transformed output object is *created and streamed* to the client in the same order, the transformation process will occur multiple times, each of which relies on one or more byte ranges of data. Let us denote the following terms:

- A web object Obj is defined as an ordered sequence {Byte(1), Byte(2), ..., Byte(i), ..., Byte(N)}, where $1 \leqslant i \leqslant N$.
- For a given web object, the transformation function X_Form occurs xT times.

The output of the ith time transformation on data in Obj can be depicted by the following formula:

$$\text{Output}(i) = \text{X\_Form}\quad (\text{Cell}(i),\ \delta(i)\text{\_S},\ \delta(i)\text{\_E},\ \text{SP},\ \text{DP},\ \text{State\_Summary}(\text{Output}(i-1)))$$

The final transformed object is given by the ordered sequence:

$$\{\text{Output}(1) \cup \text{Output}(2) \cup \ldots \cup \text{Output}(i) \cup \ldots \cup \text{Output}(xT)\}$$

And Output(i) is created only after Output(i - 1), $1 \leqslant i \leqslant xT$. The description for each of the five input parameters to X_form is given below:

Definition 5.1: Cell

A **cell** is defined as the basic unit of operation and input data range to the content transformation function X_Form to produce an output. Depending on the algorithmic nature of the transformation, its size can be very different for different applications. For example, the size can be a byte for data compression and a sentence for language translation. Without loss of generality, let us denote the cell for the ith X_form as

- Cell(i) = Ordered Sequence{Byte(Cell(i)_S), Byte(Cell(i)_S + 1), ..., Byte(Cell(i)_S + j), ..., Byte(Cell(i)_E)}, where Cell(i)_S and Cell(i)_E are the starting and ending byte positions of the cell respectively and Cell(i)_S $\leqslant$ Cell(i)_S + j $\leqslant$ Cell(i)_E.
- The size of Cell(i) is given by Size(Cell(i))= Cell(i)_E - Cell(i)_S + 1.

Note that there are xT cells for a given object with xT times transformation. Also the order of the cell sequence is defined in terms of the output seen by the client/proxy.

Data correlation describes the inter-dependence among data in the content transformation process. When a cell is being transformed, the neighborhood data before and after it might be needed to help make the transformation decision.

Definition 5.2: Correlation Range

To perform transformation on Cell(i) for Output(i) of a given object, the **correlation range** (or Corr_Range(i)), described as an ordered pair {$\delta(i)$_S, $\delta(i)$_E}, is defined as the ordered byte data sequence {byte($\delta(i)$_S), byte($\delta(i)$_S+1), ..., byte($\delta(i)$_E)} required to help in the decision making process of the transformation for Cell(i), where $\delta(i)\text{\_S} \leqslant \delta(i)\text{\_E}$. The length of the correlation range for Cell(i) is given by ($\delta(i)$_E - $\delta(i)$_S + 1).

Besides the data within a web object, most transformation processes need two sets of parameters, a static one SP and a dynamic one DP, from the environment.

Definition 5.3: Static Transformation Parameters Vector

A static transformation parameters vector SP for web content transformation is defined as the set of parameters that describe the client preference for the content transformation in the HTTP request/response headers.

Examples of the static transformation parameters include the URL being visited, language preference of the client, and the time of request, etc.

Definition 5.4: Dynamic Transformation Parameters Vector

A dynamic transformation parameters vector DP for web content transformation is defined as the set of parameters that describe the dynamic working environment for the content transformation but are not available in the HTTP request/response headers.

Examples of the dynamic transformation parameters include the simultaneous workload of the web server and the network bandwidth.

Finally, to facilitate the transformation on streaming web data, it will be good to provide a summary of what have been input and processed before and all information extracted in the transformation process.

Definition 5.5: State Summary

The state summary of the transformation State_Summary(Output(i)) with respect to Cell(i) of a web object is defined as the summary description of the previous i input and output data pairs, together with all the necessary information extracted in the previous i times transformation processes that will be needed by X_Form to produce the next Output($i + 1$). It can be described by the formula:

For $1 < i$:

State_Summary(Output(i))
= Summary_Func (Cell(i), Output(i), SP, DP,
State_Summary(Output(i - 1)))

and for $i = 1$:

State_Summary(Output(i))
= Summary_Func (Cell(i), Output(i), SP, DP)

where Summary_Func is the state summary function.

In the ideal situation, the storage requirement (or size) of the State_Summary(i) should be independent of the value of i, the number of transformation processes performed so far.

5.3 Modes of Content Transformation on Streaming Web Data

In this section, we would like to investigate the possible modes of performing real-time content transformation on the streaming data of web object. More specifically, we want to focus on the necessity and the amount of data buffering in the proxy server required by the transformation. As will be discussed in detail in Section 5.5, data buffering in the network has a direct impact on the client and proxy performance; it is also a determining factor for the feasibility and practicability of web intermediaries.

To help understand the possible modes of real-time content transformation, let us highlight some key characteristics of the current mechanism for streaming the reply data of a web request back to a client:

- In response to a web request, the data replied from a web server is sent back to a client/proxy chunk by chunk.
- The size of a data chunk is non-deterministic. While the chunk size for most Internet traffic ranges from 1.1 Kbytes to 1.3 Kbytes, the chunk size for high-speed network and intranet traffic can be as low as 100 bytes, referring to Fig. 3.14. Furthermore, it is not feasible to predefine the cut-offs of data chunks of an object statically.
- Whenever a proxy server receives a data chunk of a requested web object, it will forward it to the next network level without waiting for the whole object to arrive at the proxy first. This means that there is pipelining effect between the sending of a data chunk and the receiving of its successive ones.
- When a client receives a data chunk of a requested web object, it will interpret it immediately and will trigger the fetching of embedded objects defined inside. Just like the pipelining of data chunk transfer, this triggering of embedded object fetching will not wait for the whole object to be retrieved to the client first.

Based on the buffering requirement on the streaming web data, there are three possible modes of content transformation. They are:

- byte-streaming
- chunk-streaming
- whole-file buffering

These three modes of transformation are defined based on the relationship among the starting and ending points of the data byte range for Cell(i), correlation range Corr_Range(i) for Cell(i), and the data byte range of the chunk(s) that they are mapped to (or contained).

In the next three sub-sections, each of these three modes of content transformation will be described in detail. To make the discussion easier, let us define some notations below:

- From the viewpoint of data streaming and transmission, a web object Obj can be made up of an ordered sequence of data chunks:

$$\text{Obj} = \{\text{Chk}(1), \text{Chk}(2), \ldots, \text{Chk}(i), \ldots, \text{Chk}(M)\}$$

where Chk(i) is the ith data chunk of Obj received by the client or proxy (as input), M is the number of data chunks that make up Obj, and $1 \leqslant i \leqslant M$.

- The mapping function Pos_To_ChkNo (Byte_Loc) takes a value of byte position Byte_Loc and returns the chunk number i of Chk(i) that contains the byte at Byte_Loc.

5.3.1 Byte-Streaming Transformation Mode

In the byte-streaming mode, data is streamed through the proxy to the client just like what is observed in the current network environment. There is no extra buffering of data for the content transformation and this is true, independent of the size of the data chunk.

For all the cells Cell(i), where $1 \leqslant i \leqslant xT$ to be transformed without any kind of buffering, the pre-requisites for the byte-streaming mode to be accurately applied are:

- Pos_To_ChkNo(Cell(i)_S) = Pos_To_ChkNo(Cell(i)_E)
  - This is to ensure that the basic unit for the transformation is always contained in a single data chunk.
- Pos_To_ChkNo (δ(i)_S) = Pos_To_ChkNo(δ(i)_E) = Pos_To_ChkNo (Cell(i)_E)
  - This is to ensure that the correlation range for the transformation of Cell(i) is contained in the data chunk of Cell(i).

These pre-requisites make the byte-streaming mode practically useless because of two reasons. First, with the equations above, the possible size of a cell to be operated on is restricted by the possible size of the chunk size during data transfer. Difficulties arise because the size of a data chunk is non-deterministic and it is possible for the size to be one byte, at least in theory. Hence, in order to guarantee the correctness of transformation, the sizes of the byte range for cell and correlation also need to be one byte and they have to be the same. Second and more importantly, given a cell with a size greater than one, it is always possible for the cross-chunk phenomenon to occur. The cross-chunk phenomenon describes the situation where the starting location D_S and the ending location D_E of a data byte range D map to more than one data chunk Chk in its transfer. Figure 5.1 shows the cross-chunk phenomenon. Once again, to avoid any inaccurate transformation, this requires the size of the cell to be operated on to be one byte, which is too restrictive in most applications. Despite its non-practicability, it serves as an extreme case for our complete analysis on the modes of real-time content transformation. It also illustrates the importance of data buffering and the roots of inaccurate transformation.

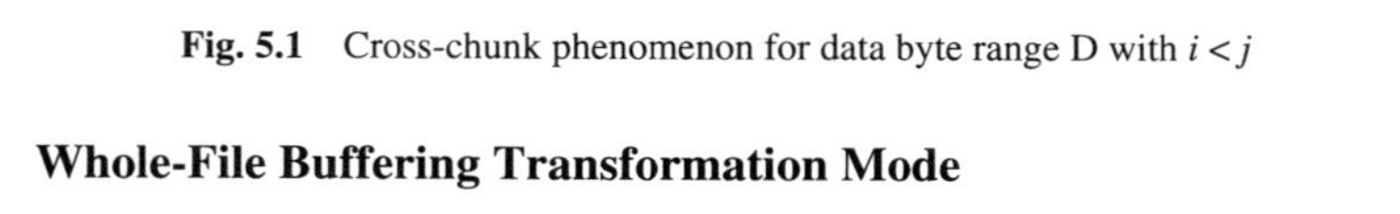

Fig. 5.1 Cross-chunk phenomenon for data byte range D with $i < j$

5.3.2 Whole-File Buffering Transformation Mode

The whole-file buffering mode for real-time content transformation is another extreme case where there exists at least one transformation process X_Form on Cell(i) such that the whole web object needs to be retrieved first before X_Form can take place. This also implies that no data Output(i) will be forwarded to the next network level (in case of the proxy) or to the browser for presentation (in case of client) unless the last chunk of the original web object Chk(M) is received and the transformation on Cell(i) is completed. Generally speaking, if this requirement is enforced, the proxy will buffer the whole object before X_Form takes place on Cell(1).

In terms of pre-requisites, this mode of transformation has the following implications:

- $\exists i \in [1 \ldots xT]$: {(Pos_To_ChkNo ($\delta(i)$_E) = Chk($M$)) or ($\delta(i)$_E = Byte($N$)), where M and N are the last chunk and byte of the object to be received by the proxy}
- The time of receiving the last byte Byte (N) of the object is less than the time of sending out the first byte of Output (i).

From the perspective of algorithmic design, this mode of content transformation is the easiest to be implemented because it is basically the same as the standalone computing environment where the entire input data file is available for computation. However, from the viewpoint of network transmission, it is the worst case as the streaming nature of the web data is completely interrupted. As we will discuss in full detail in Section 5.4, it has significant negative impact on the client/proxy performance due to the broken of data pipelining, high system resource consumption, delay of embedded object fetching, and increase in user's perceived object retrieval time.

5.3.3 Chunk-Streaming Transformation Mode

Instead of the two extreme cases, the chunk-streaming transformation mode tries to buffer just enough data chunk(s) for accurate transformation of web content and at the same time to maintain the chunk streaming nature of web data to the client. It is hoped that the upper bound size of the data needed to be buffered is small enough to be kept in the main memory and to cause negligible delay in the object/page retrieval time, thus trading off a small overhead for the potentials of performing real-time transformation on the streaming data chunks.

Assuming the number of data bytes to be buffered is at least equal to two, let us denote the range of the buffered data Buff_Data(i) needed to perform transformation on Cell(i) be {Buff(i)_S, Buff(i)_E}, where Buff(i)_S and Buff(i)_D are the starting and ending byte positions of Buff_Data(i) respectively, and Buff (i)_S $\leqslant$ Buff(i)_E.

The following relations among the starting and ending byte positions of Cell(i) and its correlation range and buffered data are given as

- Buff(i)_E = Max (Cell(i)_E, $\delta(i)$_E)
- Buff(i)_S = Min (Cell(i)_S, $\delta(i)$_S)

where Max and Min are the maximum and minimum functions for their input parameters respectively. In terms of the data chunks sent through the proxy to the client,

- The data chunk sequence to be buffered is given by
  - {Pos_To_ChkNo(Buff (i)_S), …, Pos_To_ChkNo (Buff (i)_E)}
- Total number of data chunks buffered is given by
  - Pos_To_ChkNo (Buff (i)_E) - Pos_To_ChkNo (Buff (i)_S) + 1

And for the overall buffer in the proxy, the required size is

- In terms of the number of data chunks:
  - Max($\forall i \in [1 \ldots xT]$: {Pos_To_ChkNo(Buff($i$)_E) - Pos_To_ChkNo(Buff(i)_S) + 1})
- In terms of the number of bytes:
  - (Max($\forall i \in [1 \ldots xT]$: {Pos_To_ChkNo(Buff($i$)_E) - Pos_To_ChkNo(Buff(i)_S) +

1})) × Expected_Max_Chunk_Size

Compared to the current implementation without chunk-streaming content transformation, the extra buffer requirement is

- For previous data that are read:
  - (Max(∀*i*∈[1... *xT*]: {Pos_To_ChkNo(Cell(*i*)_S) - Pos_To_ChkNo (Buff (*i*)_S) + 1})) × Expected_Max_Chunk_Size
- For future data that need to be read:
  - (Max(∀*i*∈[1... *xT*]: {Pos_To_ChkNo (Buff(*i*)_E) - Pos_To_ChkNo(Cell(*i*)_E) + 1})) × Expected_Max_Chunk_Size

In actual implementation, if only one extra chunk of data is buffered to handle the cross-chunk effect, it will be the "realistic" ideal situation.

5.4 Discussion of the Impact of Transformation Mode on Web Page Latency

In the last section, we propose three possible modes of performing real-time content transformation on the streaming data of web object. We also give the pre-requisites and buffer requirements for them to be applied and implemented. In this section, we would like to analyze their implications to the client/proxy performance. Since the byte-streaming mode is not really practical (due to the cross-chunk effect), our comparison will be focused on the whole-file buffering and the chunk-streaming transformation modes.

Without loss of generality, in the rest of the section, let us assume the comparison reference to be the chunk-streaming transformation mode that needs only one extra chunk of data buffering. In the analysis, we would like to investigate the effect of the whole-file buffering transformation mode on:

- interruption of streaming data pipelining
- embedded object (perceived) retrieval latency
- page retrieval latency
- system resource consumption

To understand the impact of buffering streaming data in the proxy on content transformation, let us turn to our chunk-level dependence model and find out exactly what happens to the web data when such buffering occurs. Under the streaming mode of web data transfer, the sending of the previous data chunk Chk(*i* - 1) to the next network level and the receiving of the current data chunk Chk(*i*) from the web content server are likely to be overlapping to each other, thus resulting in a certain degree of pipelining on data transfer. This is represented in our C-LDG as a single chunk node Chk(*i*). Furthermore, whenever a data chunk is received, it will be forwarded immediately to the next network level (or displayed to the client) without waiting for subsequent data chunks to arrive.

When the whole-file buffering transformation is applied to the streaming web data, the data pipelining will be broken because the reading of the streaming data needs to be finished before any data forwarding to the next network level can occur. In the C-LDG, we call this the **node splitting effect.** Each chunk node Chk(i) in the C-LDG is split into two sub-nodes, one for read/receiving (or Chk(i)_R) and one for write/forwarding (or Chk(i)_W). This is shown in Fig. 5.2(a) and (b). The node splitting or interruption of the data transfer pipelining definitely increases the transfer time of web object retrieval. Depending on the relative magnitudes of the reading and forwarding times of the data chunk, its impact on the object transfer time might vary. The worst case occurs when the two values are comparable with each other.

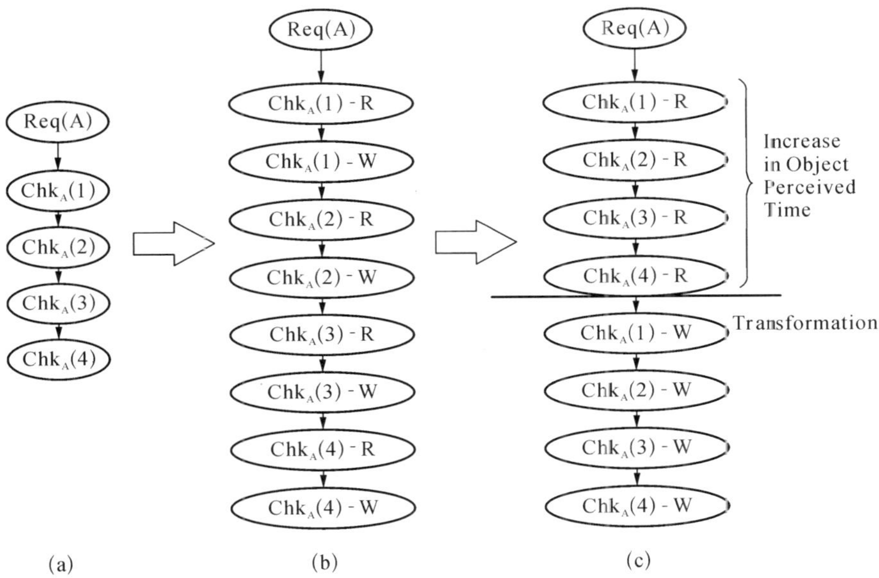

Fig. 5.2 Node splitting and regrouping effects in C-LDG due to whole-file buffering

The second direct effect of the whole-file buffering transformation is the regrouping of the split nodes in the C-LDG. Since all the data need to be received first before any transformation can take place and its result can be forwarded to the next client/proxy level, all the Chk(i)_R nodes are moved forward and grouped together, followed by the Chk(i)_W nodes. In the C-LDG, we call this the **regrouping effect**. Continuing with the example in Fig. 5.2, the regrouping effect is shown in Fig. 5.2(c), where all the write/forwarding nodes Chk_A (i)_W are moved after the last chunk read node Chk_A(4)_R. Obviously, this regrouping effect has a great impact on the client's perceived time of object retrieval. The object perceived time is increased significantly.

The third direct effect of the whole-file buffering transformation is related to the retrieval of embedded objects inside a page. If the transformation is applied to the container object of a web page, its content will be interpreted only after its last read/receiving node Chk(M) has arrived. In other words, the triggering of embedded object retrieval is now being pushed backward from the read/receiving node Chk(i)_R that defines the object to the write/forwarding node Chk(i)_W. We call this the **push-**

backward effect. Figure 5.3(c) shows the push-backward effect on the retrieval of object B due to the transformation on object A. Just opposite to the push-forward effect that we discussed in Chapter 4, the push-backward effect has a significant negative effect to page retrieval time.

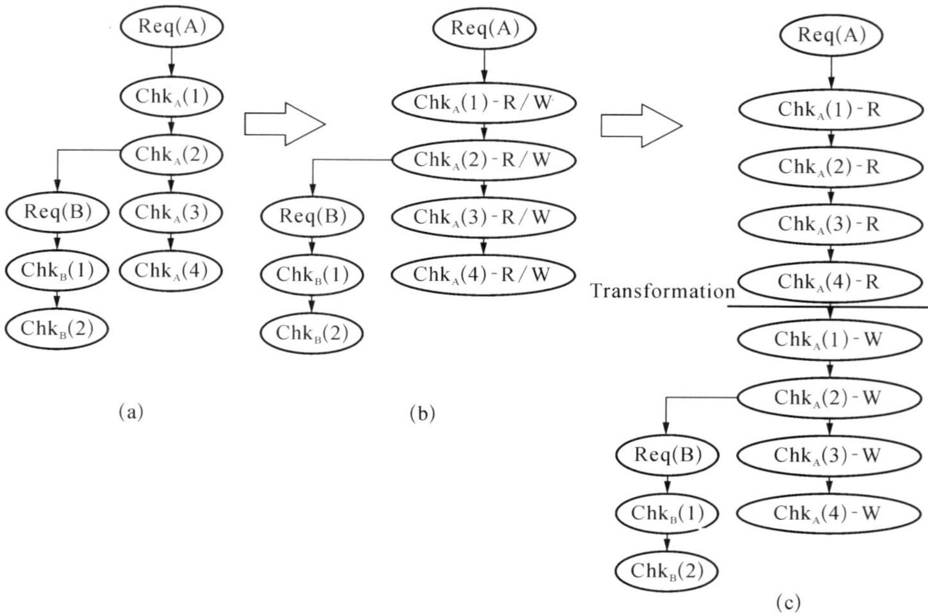

Fig. 5.3 Push-backward effect in C-LDG due to whole-file buffering

In additions to the above three node splitting, regrouping, and push-backward effects, the whole-file buffering mode of transformation also has an impact on the system resource consumption, which in turn brings a further negative effect on the client/proxy performance. Buffering the whole file for transformation increases the memory demand significantly, especially since there is no upper bound to the size of a web object. This is likely to result in more memory swapping and disk I/O operations. For proxy server with large number of simultaneous connections, this definitely degrades the performance of proxy server significantly, both in terms of the number of simultaneous connections and the object retrieval time.

5.5 Experimental Study

Just like the acceleration mechanisms proposed in Chapter 4, we would like to conduct similar sets of experiments to find out the effects of whole-file buffering transformation on client/proxy performance. All the setups, experimental environment, and assumptions are the same as those in Chapter 4. Once again, the measuring parameters for the experiments are the object and page retrieval times. Note that in our study here, since the primary focus is page retrieval time, the perceived retrieval time of an object is measured with respect to the request time of its page container object, the same assumption that we make in Chapter 4.

5.5.1 Regrouping and Push-Backward Effects on Object Perceived Time

To understand the effect of the whole-file buffering transformation on client/proxy performance, we would like to first find out its effect on the object perceived time. Figure 5.4 shows the distribution of the normalized perceived time of objects with parallelism width of four. The normalized perceived time of object is defined as

Without regrouping and push-backward effects (i.e. original one):

$$\frac{Object\_Percieved\_Time\_Container\_Object\_Request\_Time}{Original\_Page\_Retreival\_Time} \times 100\%$$

With regrouping and push-backward effects:

$$\frac{Object\_Percieved\_Time\_With\_Push\_Backward\_Container\_Object\_Request\_Time}{Original\_Page\_Retreival\_Time\_Without\_Push\_Backward} \times 100\%$$

The reference to this definition is page retrieval time instead of object retrieval time or object perceived time. We believe that this can give a better, realistic picture of what happens to object perceived time as seen by a client.

Figure 5.4 shows the result of the distribution before and after regrouping and push-backward effects. The x axis is normalized object perceived time and the y axis is the distribution. From Fig.5.4, we see that in the original situation (i.e. without regrouping and push-backward effects), about half of the objects have quite a long perceived time. This is expected because of the limited parallelism width for simultaneous object fetching and the dependence of embedded objects definition with respect to their page container object. The other half of the objects mainly refers to those pages with single object. The observed average perceived time of objects is 24.1% for Berkeley data, 28.6% for Digital data, and 16.7% for NLANR data.

With regrouping and push-backward effects, the distribution of the normalized perceived time of object shifts to the right by about 10% to 20%. The average perceived time of objects also changes to 33.2% for Berkeley, 35.0% for Digital, and 27.57% for NLANR. This big increase in the average perceived time of object (37.8% for Berkeley, 22.4% for Digital, and 64.8% for NLANR) supports our argument that the chunk-streaming transformation mode is preferred over the whole-file transformation mode, despite its complexity in implementation.

One interesting observation in Fig. 5.4 is that about 10% of the objects have a perceived time greater than the original page retrieval time after regrouping and push-backward effects are applied. This can be explained easily by the actual increase in page retrieval time, as we will discuss in next sub-section.

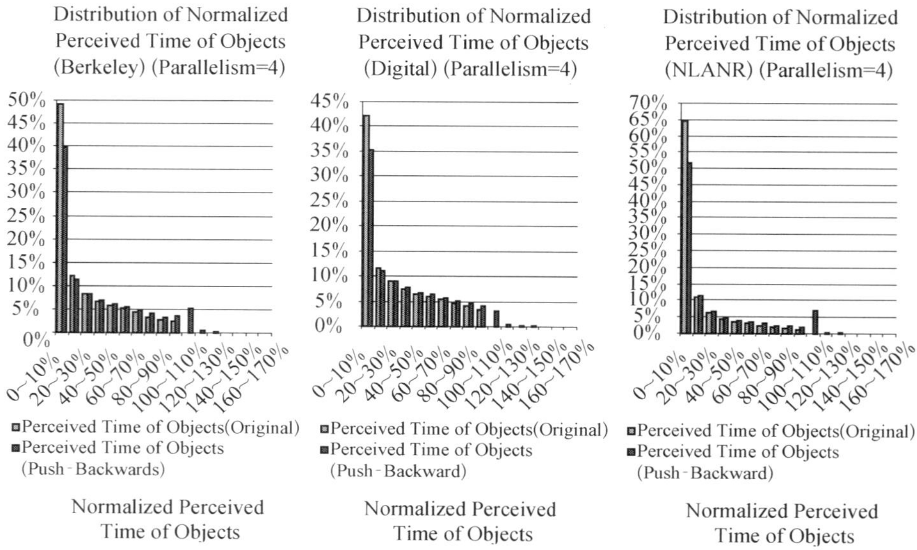

Fig. 5.4 Distribution of normalized perceived time of objects (with respect to page container object request time) before and after regrouping/push-backward effects, and parallelism width = 4

5.5.2 Regrouping and Push-Backward Effects on Page Retrieval Time

Next, we would like to understand the regrouping and push-backward effects of the whole-file buffering transformation on page retrieval time. This study is important because this is the actual delay seen by the client. The increase in normalized page retrieval time due to regrouping and push-backward effects is defined as

$$\frac{Page\_Retrieval\_Time\_With\_Regrouping/Push\_Backward - Original\_Page\_Retrieval\_Time}{Original\_Page\_Retrieval\_Time} \times 100\%$$

The result of the increase in normalized page retrieval time due to regrouping and push-backward effects is shown in Fig.5.5 where the x axis is the increase in normalized page retrieval time and the y axis is the distribution. Here we see that while 78% to 85% of the pages have their retrieval time increased by less than 10%, the rest of the pages have their retrieval times increased significantly. On average, the increase in page retrieval time due to the regrouping and push-backward effects is 9.8% for Berkeley data, 9.2% for Digital data, and 12.3% for NLANR data. Table 5.1 shows the summary of the impact of the regrouping and push-backward effects on object perceived time and page retrieval time.

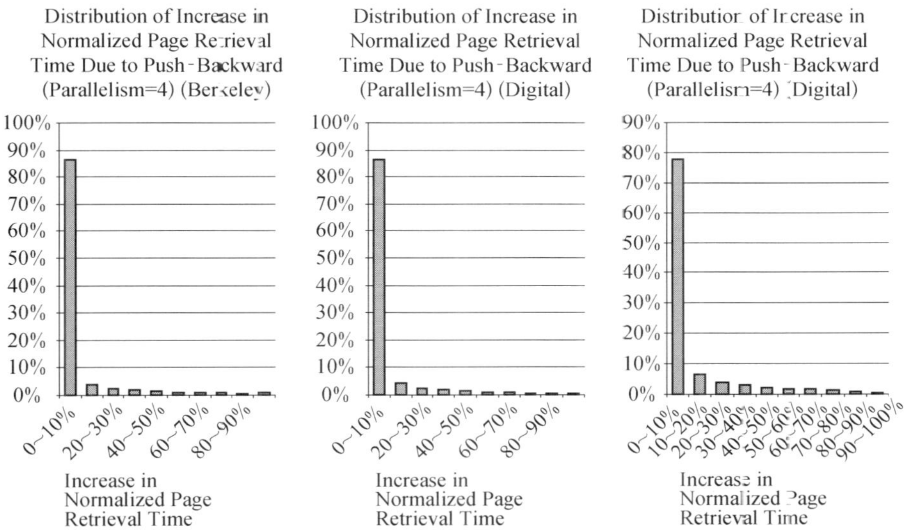

Fig. 5.5 Distribution of increase in normalized page retrieval time due to regrouping and push-backward effects and parallelism width=4

Table 5.1 Impact of Regrouping and Push-Backward Effects on Object Perceived Time and Page Retrieval Time

	Berkeley	Digital	NLANR
Average Perceived Time of Object	24.099,6%	28.610,4%	16.723,9%
Average Perceived Time of Object with Regrouping and Push-Backward Effect	33.209,9%	35.013,7%	27.567,3%
Increase in Average Retrieval Time Due to Regrouping and Push-Backward Effect	37.802,7%	22.381,0%	64.837,7%
Increase in Page Retrieval Time due to Regrouping and Push-Backward Effect	9.836,3%	9.216,9%	12.285,4%

The significant increase in page retrieval time further supports our argument that whole-file buffering transformation should be used only if it is really necessary. In the situation where the transformation is only used to speed up the downloading of web pages, its cost-effectiveness will be questionable.

5.5.3 Regrouping and Push-Backward Effects in the Presence of Proxy Cache

The last set of experiments we would like to conduct is to find out the impact of regrouping and push-backward effects on page retrieval time in the presence of proxy cache. The configurations and mechanisms of the proxy cache used here are similar to those used in Chapter 4.

The increase in normalized page retrieval time due to regrouping and push-backward effects is defined as

$$1-\frac{\sum Original\_Page\_Latency\_Without\_Regrouping\_and\_Push\_Backward\_and\_With\_\mathrm{Proxy}\_Cache}{\sum Page\_Latency\_With\_Regrouping\_and\_Push\_Backward\_and\_With\_Same\_\mathrm{Proxy}\_Cache}$$

The result is shown in Fig. 5.6 where the x axis is the proxy cache, defined in terms of the percentage of the total unique object size in the trace and the y axis is the increase in normalized page retrieval time. The result shows that due to the sharing and reuse of objects among web pages, normalized page retrieval time is increased by 2.5% to 5% which is slightly lower than what we show in Table 5.1 without proxy cache. Despite the smaller percentage, we argue that the chunk-streaming transformation mode is still highly preferred than the whole-file buffering transformation mode because of the large increase in the object perceived time and the extra consumption in system resource (such as Disk I/Os). Furthermore, the 2.5% to 5% performance is significantly enough not to be ignored. Just like the push-forward situation, the increase in normalized page retrieval time decreases with increasing cache size, which is quite reasonable (due to more cache hits on the embedded objects of a page).

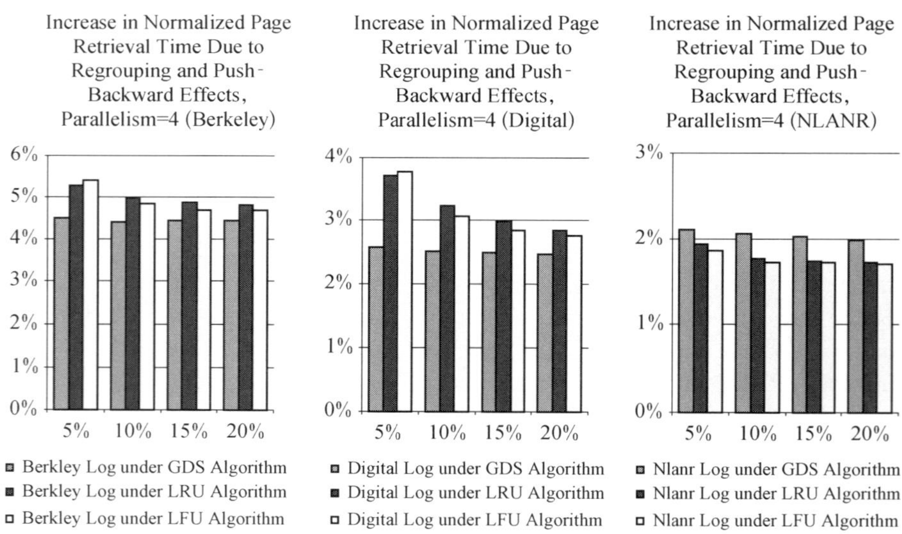

Fig. 5.6 Increase in normalized page retrieval time due to regrouping and push-backward effects and parallelism width = 4

Finally, we would like to find out the sensitivity of our observed results with respect to the parallelism width for simultaneous object fetching. The result is shown in Fig. 5.7, where the x axis is now the parallelism width instead of the cache size.

Figure 5.7 shows that the observation on the increase in normalized page retrieval time due to regrouping and push-backward effects is generally true, independent of the parallelism width available for simultaneous object fetching.

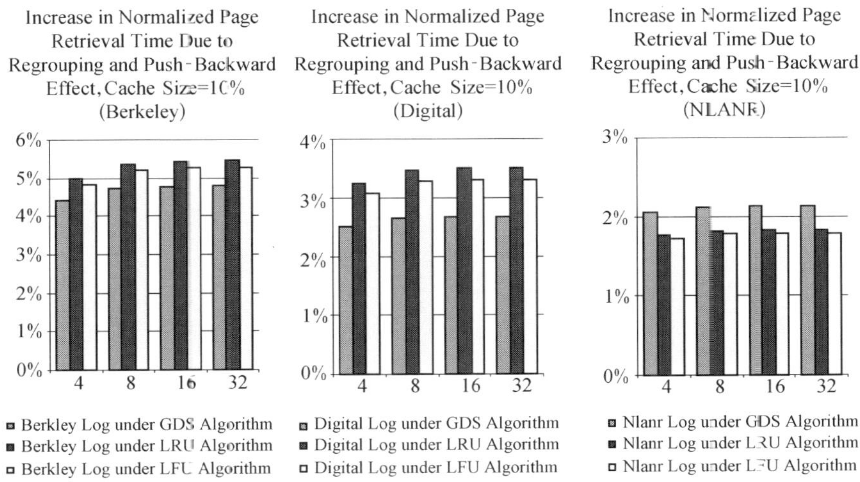

Fig. 5.7 Increase in normalized page retrieval time due to regrouping and push-backward effects and cache size = 10%

5.6 Conclusion

In this chapter, we propose three basic modes of conducting real-time content transformation on streaming web data. They are the byte-streaming, chunk-streaming, and whole-file buffering. We argue that the chunk-streaming transformation mode is superior to the other two modes because of its practicability and its lower impact on client/proxy performance. We further analyze the performance of the whole-file buffering transformation mode by introducing the concepts of node-splitting, regrouping, and push-backward in the C-LDG. Experimental result is also given to support our argument on and analysis of the pros and cons of the modes of transformation.

References

(Fox et al. 1998) Fox A, Gribble S D, Chawathe Y et al. (1998) Adapting to Network and Client Variation Using Active Proxies: Lessons and perspectives. IEEE Personal Communications 5: 10-19

(ICAP 2010) ICAP-Forum 2010. Internet Content Adaptation Protocol (I-CAP). http://www.icap-forum.org. Accessed 14 April, 2010

(OPES 2001) Open Pluggable Edges Services(OPES) (2001) http://datatracker.ietf.org/wg/opes/charter. Accessed 14 April, 2010

(TRACE 2001) Proxy Trace achieved in NLANR. ftp://ftp.ircache.net. Accessed 14 April, 2010

(Walser and Hager 2001) Walser K, Hager J (2001) Future of Internet Appliances, Technology Brief 1(6), July 2001

6

System Framework for Web Content Adaptation and Intermediary Services: Design and Implementation

6.1 Introduction

In chapters, we discuss the transformation model for real-time content adaptation and transformation in proxy cache. Two realistic models, chunk streaming and whole file buffering, are proposed and their pros and cons are analyzed. We also highlight some of the basic requirements for them to be adopted in real proxy cache.

In this chapter, we would like to go further and look into the details of the design consideration and implementation for real-time content adaptation and transformation to take place in proxy caches. Two key aspects of this "active proxy cache" are emphasized. First, due to the streaming nature of web data chunks, we would like to find out at which stage of the data transfer a given content adaptation and transformation process should take place so that the greatest cost-effectiveness can be achieved. By cost-effectiveness, we refer to the cost of performing content transformation and caching the transformed object vs. the saving from reusing a cached, transformed object in future. Second, from the viewpoint of a proxy cache, we would like to discuss the tasks and the special handling of system process that real-time content transformation and adaptation needs from the HTTP protocols and the management of the proxy cache systems.

To make the discussion more concrete, we would use the SQUID proxy cache (SQUID) as an example platform to explain how the HTTP protocol and system issues due to the real-time content transformation and adaptation should be handled. SQUID is chosen to be the discussion platform because it is the most widely deployed proxy cache with open source code. The implementation of real-time content adaptation of SQUID not only gives insight into what can possibly happen in a real proxy but also provides a platform for new technologies and protocols to be experimented on.

This chapter focuses on the generic proxy cache system architecture for web intermediary services with real-time content adaptation. Then in the next chapter, we will use the automatic watermarking proxy-based system to further illustrate what we discuss in this chapter.

The outline for the rest of the chapter is as follows. First, we briefly describe the dataflow of a proxy cache and use SQUID as the discussion example. Then a four-stage transformation framework, called the **4-Stage AXform Framework**, is proposed to study the mapping of a given content transformation function onto one of the four possible stages along the dataflow path of the streaming web data. The availability of information required to make the content transformation decision, the caching of the transformed information and its possible reuse, and the nature of typical transformation to take place efficiently are the main focuses of the discussion. Sample examples of the real-time content adaptation and transformation at each stage are also given. Finally, the system architecture for real-time content adaptation and transformation in proxy is analyzed. Typical system issues in the implementation of the AXform framework are discussed.

6.2 Basic Proxy Cache

Before we give a detailed discussion of the system design and implementation issues for real-time content transformation on proxy cache, it will be helpful to have an understanding of how a proxy cache works, together with its associated dataflow path. In the next two sub-sections, the typical dataflow of a proxy cache will be given, followed by a concrete example of the dataflow for the request processing in SQUID.

6.2.1 DataFlow Path of Proxy Cache

A proxy cache is located between a web client and a web server. Independent of how it is set up as a forward or reverse proxy server, a proxy cache is a middleware in the network, forwarding the web request from a client to a web server and streaming the replied data chunks back from the server to the client. Caching of the replied data into the proxy is also done whenever possible. Figure 6.1 depicts the typical dataflow of a proxy cache server. To emphasize on the dataflow and caching effect of the proxy, some modules (such as the DNS lookup and network connection ICP module) that are not directly related to the real-time content adaptation and transformation in proxy are not included in the discussion below. Readers interested in those topics can refer to (Wessels 2001). In Fig. 6.1, the modules inside the dashed square box are the main caching functions of the proxy.

The dataflow of a proxy cache can be summarized as follows. Upon arrival of a request from a web client, the proxy cache will check it against its local storage. One of the following three situations might happen:

Case I: Full Cache Hit Without Validation

The requested object is found in the local storage of the proxy cache and its expire time has not passed yet (i.e. its content is still valid). In this case, the cached copy of the object will be retrieved from the local cache and be delivered to the client. The dataflow path of this case follows the steps:

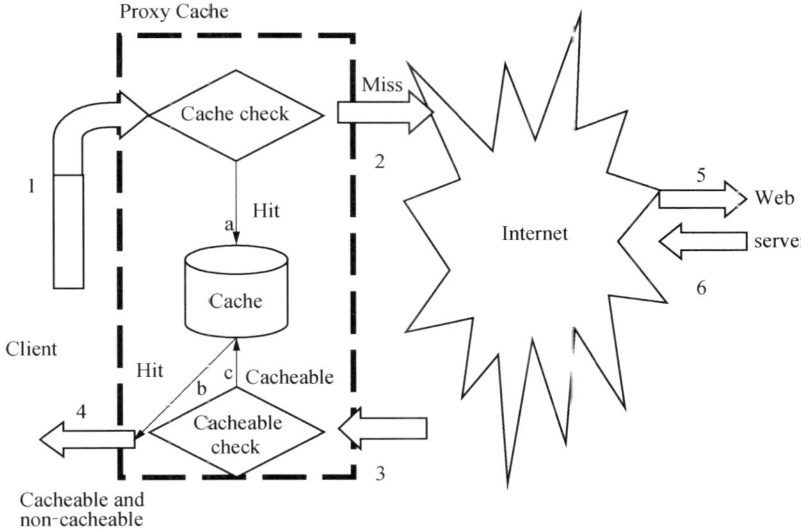

Fig. 6.1 Typical data flow of a proxy cache

$$\textit{Client} \rightarrow 1 \rightarrow a \rightarrow b \rightarrow 4 \rightarrow \textit{Client}$$

Case II: Cache Hit With Validation

The requested object is found in the local cache storage, but the proxy cache is not sure whether the cached copy of the data is valid. According to the HTTP protocol, the proxy will send an IMS (if-modified-since) request to the original server to validate the freshness of the local cached copy of the object. Two sub-cases can happen:

- *Case II (a): Content of the local cached copy of the object is valid*

The local copy of the data is fresh and is the same as that in the original web server. In this case, the original web server will respond with an HTTP 304 reply to the proxy. Then the proxy will forward the cached copy of the object to the client. The dataflow path of this case follows the steps:

$$\textit{Client} \rightarrow 1 \rightarrow 2 \rightarrow 5 \rightarrow \textit{Web Server} \rightarrow 6 \rightarrow 3 \rightarrow b \rightarrow 4 \rightarrow \textit{Client}$$

- *Case II (b): Content of the local cached copy of the object is invalid*

The local copy of the data is outdated and the object has been modified since its last retrieval to the proxy cache. In this case, the original web server will send the full object to the client through the proxy cache in a chunk-by-chunk manner. The dataflow path of this case is the same as that of Case III for cache miss below. Note that although the dataflow path in this case is similar to that of Case II (a), the amount of information transferred is different.

Case III: Cache Miss

This situation occurs when either the requested object is not found in cache or the cached copy of the object is outdated (or invalid). In this case, the proxy communicates with the original web server to retrieve the most updated copy of the requested object. The object is then streamed back from the web server, through the proxy, to the client in a chunk-by-chunk manner. At the same time, the proxy will also determine if the requested object is cacheable. For a cacheable object, a copy of it will be stored in the local proxy cache for possible future reuse. The dataflow path of this case follows the steps:

Client → 1 → 2 → 5 → Web Server → 6 → 3 → 4 (also c for cacheable object) → Client

Note that step "c" is also involved in the dataflow path for those cacheable objects that will be stored in the proxy cache.

6.2.2 DataFlow Path in SQUID Proxy Cache

To make our discussion more concrete and to help understand the real situation of data chunks flowing through the proxy cache, the basic steps involved in processing a client request in SQUID are given below. Just like any generic proxy cache, the data are transferred through the SQUID chunk-by-chunk. Whenever the SQUID receives a chunk of data from its upper network level, it will forward the data chunk to the next level of the client/proxy immediately without waiting for the whole data object to come first.

The description below is based on the SQUID proxy version 2.1. Basically, there are two phases to a client request: Request and Reply.

6.2.2.1 Phase 1: Request Processing

The Request processing can be described roughly as a seven steps process:

[1] <u>Client Connection:</u>

When a proxy server receives a request from a client, it will respond to the request by establishing a connection to the client.

Function call(s) in SQUID: asciiHandleConn()

[2] <u>Request Decoding:</u>

The received HTTP request is read and parsed in the proxy server.

Function call(s) in SQUID: clientReadRequest(), parseHttpRequest()

[3] <u>Access Control:</u>

The access control of the proxy involves the checking of the requested IP address and domain name with a pre-defined list of URL addresses. It might also use the dnsserver program to get the DNS results if they are not in the ip_cache. The client-side of the proxy will build an ACL state data structure and register a callback function for notification when the access control checking is completed.

Function call(s) in SQUID: clientAccessCheck(), clientAccessCheckDone()

[4] <u>Cache Hit/Miss:</u>

After the access control is passed, the proxy will look for the requested object in its local cache. If there is a cache hit, the client-side of the proxy will register the information in the StoreEntry. Otherwise, the SQUID will forward the request to the Web server/proxy in the next network level.

Function call(s) in SQUID: clientProcessRequest(), clientProcessMISS()

[5] ICP Probing:

The request-forwarding process begins with protoDispatch(). This function is a peer selection procedure, which may involve sending ICP queries and receiving ICP replies. After the ICP replies (if any) are processed, protoStart() will start. This function calls an appropriate protocol-specific function to forward the request

Function call(s) in SQUID: protoDispatch(), protoStart()

[6] HTTP Connection:

The HTTP module first opens a connection to the origin server or the next level cache peer. Then, a new connection request is passed to the Network Communication Module with a callback function. The comm.c routine may try to establish a connection multiple times before it gives up.

Function call(s) in SQUID: httpStart(), httpConnect()

[7] HTTP Communication:

After a TCP connection is established, the HTTP will build a request buffer and submit it for writing onto the socket. It then registers a read handler to receive and process the HTTP reply.

Function call(s) in SQUID: httpConnectDone(), httpSendRequest(), httpSendComplete()

6.2.2.2 Phase 2: Reply Processing

The Reply processing can be described roughly as a six steps process:

[1] Reply Setup:

When a reply is received by the proxy server, its HTTP reply header will be parsed and be placed into a reply data structure.

Function call(s) in SQUID: httpReadReply(), httpParseReplyHeader()

[2] Data Receiving:

As the reply data is read by the proxy server, it will be appended to the StoreEntry. The client-side of the proxy is then notified of the new data via a callback function.

Function call(s) in SQUID: storeAppend(), invokeHandles()

[3] Client Data Streaming:

After the client-side of the proxy is notified of the new data, it will copy the data from the StoreEntry and submit it for writing on the client socket. The reply header is also built.

Function call(s) in SQUID: clientSendMoreData(), clientBuildReply()

[4] Local Data Storage:

While the receiving data is appended to the StoreEntry, and is streamed to the client(s), the data may be submitted to the proxy for writing onto the disk.

Function call(s) in SQUID: storeClientCopy()

[5] End of Data Streaming:

When the HTTP module finishes reading the reply data from the upstream server, it will mark the StoreEntry as "complete". Then the server socket is closed.

Function call(s) in SQUID: storeComplete(), comm_close(server socket)

[6] Disconnection of Request:

When the client-side of the proxy server has finished writing all the object data in its local disk, it will un-register itself from the StoreEntry and will free up all resource variables. At the same time, it also closes the client connection.

Function call(s) in SQUID: httpStateFree(), comm_close(client socket), icpStateFree

6.3 Four-Stage AXform Framework

With the basic understanding of the dataflow path for the basic proxy cache described in the last section, we can now look into the real-time content adaptation and transformation process that can take place on the streaming web data as it passes through the proxy. From the viewpoint of a proxy cache, the dataflow path can be divided naturally into four segments:

- client request to proxy cache
- proxy cache request to web server
- web server data reply to proxy cache
- proxy cache data reply to client

These four segments are shown in Fig. 6.1 as the dataflow point 1 to 4 respectively.

To study the real-time content transformation and adaptation in proxy cache in a more symmetric way, we propose a **4-stage AXform framework** for web intermediaries in this chapter. The four stages of the framework are shown in Fig. 6.2. They are

- Stage 1: Client Request Stage
- Stage 2: Server Request Stage
- Stage 3: Server Data Stage
- Stage 4: Client Data Stage

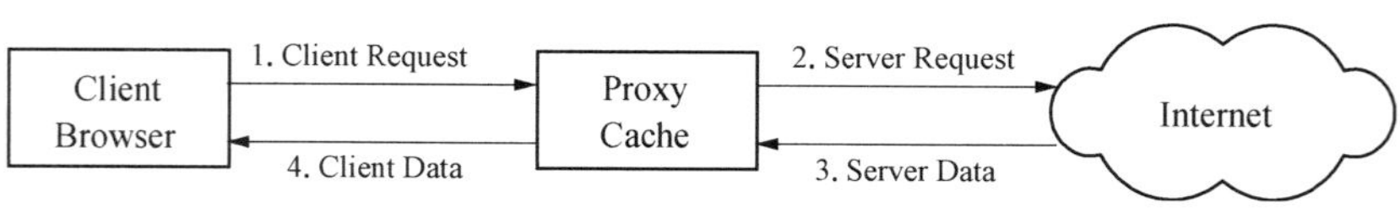

Fig. 6.2 4-Stage AXform framework for web intermediaries

Clearly, there is a direct one-to-one correspondence between the stages in the framework and the segments along the web transfer datapath. Referring to Fig. 6.1, the first stage, *Client Request Stage,* occurs at the dataflow point 1, where a proxy receives a request from a web client. The second stage, *Server Request Stage,* occurs at the dataflow point 2 where the proxy sends out the request to the original web server. The third stage, *Server Data Stage,* occurs at the dataflow point 3 where the proxy gets the reply data from the web server. The fourth stage, *Client Data Stage,* occurs at the dataflow point 4 where the proxy sends the reply data to the web client.

A given content transformation and adaptation function might take place in one or more stages in the AXform framework. The choice of the stage(s) for a transformation function to take place has direct impacts on its performance overhead, cost effectiveness, and implementation difficulties. This is due to the unique properties of each stage of the framework, which include

- Data availability for content transformation.
- Availability of the original and transformed content of an object in the proxy cache for possible future data reuse.
- The possibility of bypassing the transformation process in the case of a full local proxy cache hit. (Note that in case of a cache hit, Stage 2 and 3 of the AXform framework will be bypassed in the dataflow path).

In the next four sub-sections, each of the four stages will be analyzed in detail. The focus of the discussion will be on how the availability of the data and the caching issue on the original and transformed object data will affect the applicability, suitability and the cost-effectiveness of a given transformation function. Sample case studies will also be given to illustrate our argument.

To help clarifying the concept without losing generosity, the discussion only focuses on the HTTP request and reply and only one proxy cache exists between the client and the web server.

6.3.1 Stage 1 of AXform Framework: Client Request Stage

The client request stage of the AXform framework starts when the request from a web client reaches the proxy cache and ends when the request is completely received by the proxy. Possible transformation might take place on the request data during its arrival in the proxy. Note that this stage does not include the datapath of either forwarding the request to the server (in case of a proxy cache miss) or sending the reply object data to the client from the local cache (in case of a proxy cache hit).

6.3.1.1 Input Data Availability and Output

At this stage, the proxy cache gets the full HTTP request from the client. Thus all the HTTP request header information such as the HTTP method, requested URL, content negotiation message, …, etc. are made known to the proxy at this stage. Other TCP/IP information, including the client's DNS and IP address is also available. At the same time, the proxy cache has information about the characteristics of the environment it operates on. Examples of such characteristics are system workload, network speed, bandwidth availability, and system time. This can be obtained by periodically monitoring the network and server environment. In the case of the POST method, the body data of the HTTP request is also available for transformation and adaptation.

Independent of the type of transformation and adaptation taken place at this stage, the output data should be a valid HTTP request (i.e. the integrity of the HTTP request has to be preserved). This is because the output needs to be passed to either the original web server for data or Stage 4 of the framework to serve the client with the cached copy of the requested data.

The transformed output might include changes in the attributes of an HTTP request (such as the requested IP destination) as well as the data body in case of a POST request.

The proxy will then determine if it should forward the transformed request to the original web server (in case of a cache miss) or it should serve the client with the local cached copy of the data (in case of a cache hit).

6.3.1.2 Caching Issue

Caching issue is always one of the most important, yet difficult problems in real-time content transformation and adaptation in the proxy. It determines the possible reuse of the original and transformation object data in the local cache, which in turn, determines the network bandwidth consumption, the correctness of the delivered content (original vs. transformed object), and the demand for proxy server's computation power.

In this stage, there is no caching problem because the transformation takes place before any checking of the proxy cache. All the client request and their possible POST data will pass through the transformation module. There is no reuse of previously transformed client request and their possible POST data.

6.3.1.3 Appropriateness of Content Transformation

The appropriateness of a content transformation process at a given stage of the AXform framework is directly related to the possible information available at that stage. The information source might come from the current request and reply or from the previously accessed, cached data copy from the proxy.

At this stage, since the information available are mainly those in the header fields of an HTTP request, any transformation or adaptation taken place will be related to the modification of the request header fields. That is, based on the client information and the operation environment parameters, a subset of the header fields in an HTTP request will be adjusted to make the request more appropriate either for the client or for the server. This includes the approval or denial of the request for a given user. Examples of sample transformation at this stage include client IP-based redirection and anonymous web access.

Without the possibility of reusing any previously transformed client request and the POST body data, personalization of a client request based on the updating of any network and web server related information can be done more accurately. However, the same reason also makes the overhead of transformation relatively higher than if the transformation takes place in the Stage 2 of the AXform framework (see Section 6.3.2.3).

One thing worth mentioning here is the emerging peer-to-peer computing over the traditional client-server structure. With this new concept, it is expected that a larger HTTP request with content body will appear in this stage. This will in turn create more opportunities for content-based transformation to occur in this stage.

6.3.1.4 Case Study: Client IP-Based Redirection

To help understand the client request stage of the AXform framework better, the client IP-based redirection is given here to illustrate how the header information of a web request can be modified.

Redirection of web request is quite common in the network. In the past, the redirection takes place in the web server where it returns an HTTP redirect reply to a client, transferring the client's request to another server for content retrieval. This is usually done for the purpose of load-balancing. However, with the setting up of content delivery network services, the role of performing request redirection is now shifted to the edge proxy server. This results in the client IP/DNS-based direction of web request. For this kind of redirection, we introduce an HTTP header rewriter in the client request stage of the AXform framework to modify the header fields of the web request.

Figure 6.3 shows an example of the client IP-based redirection of web request through a request header rewriter. Its working principle is as follows: At the client request stage, the client HTTP request is passed to the request header rewriter module. Based on the client IP and some predefined rules, the requested URL will be revised. New URL information will be updated in the header fields so that the client request will be made to the new redirected location. Note that the whole process is transparent to the client.

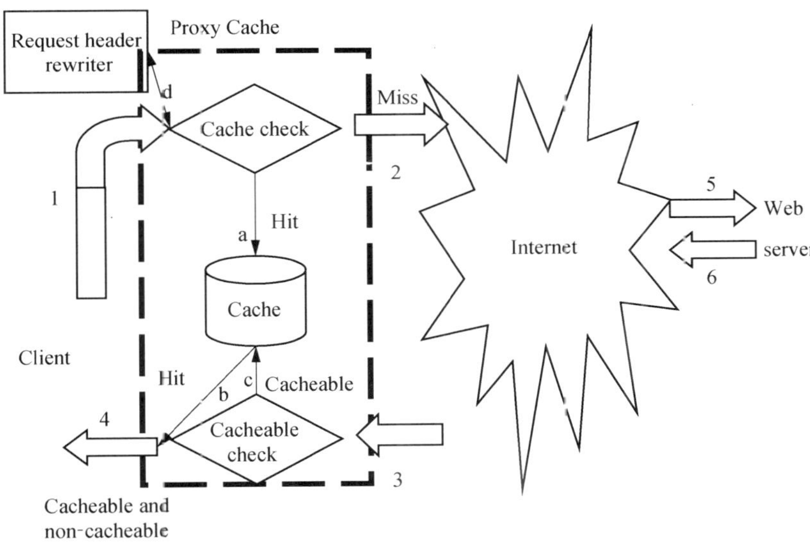

Fig. 6.3 Client IP-based redirection of web request at Stage 1 of AXform framework

One thing worth mentioning here is that after the transformation, the new request will go through the proxy cache check, just like other normal HTTP requests. Thus, if the new request is found in cache, it will be served as a cache hit, independent of whether the original request is a cache hit or miss.

6.3.2 Stage 2 of AXform Framework: Server Request Stage

The server request Stage of the 4-Stage AXform framework starts when the client request starts to be sent out from the proxy to the original web server (or the next level of the network) and ends when the request is completely received by the web server. Possible transformation can take place on the client's request data during its transfer from the proxy to the web server. Note that if a web client request is a valid hit in the proxy cache, this stage will not be triggered.

6.3.2.1 Input Data Availability and Output

Besides the additional caching information of a client request, all the HTTP request header information available at Stage 1 of the AXform framework are also available in this server request Stage (or Stage 2) as input. This can possibly include any transformed header information inserted in the client request if content transformation also takes place at Stage 1.

Similar to Stage 1, the transformed output of this stage includes all the changes in the header fields of the request. It will be a valid HTTP request, being forwarded by the proxy to the original web server.

6.3.2.2 Caching Issue

At Stage 2 of the AXform framework, a client's HTTP request has already passed through the proxy cache check module. Caching effect to the transformation and adaptation on the client request data will show in the following ways:

- If the client's requested URL from the output of Stage 1 is found in the proxy cache, Stage 2 of the framework will not be triggered.
- In case of the proxy cache hit for the client request, previously transformed request data will be reused, being forwarded to the client through Stage 4 of the framework and bypassing Stage 2.
- In case of the proxy cache miss for the client request, Stage 2 transformation will take place on the client's HTTP request during its transfer from the proxy to the web server.

6.3.2.3 Appropriateness of Content Transformation

The input data availability of Stage 1 and Stage 2 of the AXform framework is very similar. As a result, we expect similar types of content transformation and adaptation to take place in these two stages. All are related on the modification of the client's HTTP request information. Sample transformation functions at this stage are access control, request filtering, ... etc.

However, in terms of the appropriateness of a given content transformation on a client's request, the two stages differ significantly. This is due to the possible reuse of the previously transformed request data in case of a proxy cache hit.

Reuse of the previously transformed client request data is sometimes helpful, especially when the transformation process is time consuming. This can also save the computation power of the proxy server and the network bandwidth consumption. On the other hand, the same data reuse also makes request personalization difficult.

As an example, the client IP/DNS-based redirect mentioned in Section 6.3.1.4 should not be done at Stage 2. Suppose two different clients sending request with the same URL. According to the requirement of the redirect approach, they should go to different web servers for service. However, if the transformation is done at Stage 2 and assuming the requested object is cacheable, they might end up serving by the same web server.

Hence, as a general guideline, personalization of client request data should be done at Stage 1 whereas the "universal" adaptation (i.e. independent of client/network/server preferences) of client request data should be conducted at Stage 2 of the framework.

6.3.2.4 Case Study: URL Based Access Control

To help understand the server request stage of the AXform framework better, the URL based access control is used to illustrate how the header information of a web request can be modified and how the previously transformed result can be reused.

Access control such as content filtering and blocking is quite common in today's Internet deployment. The idea is to protect a given group of clients or the use of network resource through some restrictions to the Internet access. For example, in the education environment, students are protected from Internet pornography through URL filtering and blocking. A database of pre-defined, forbidden web site URL list is maintained in the proxy server and the access control policy is enforced through the matching of the requested URL against this forbidden URL list.

Figure 6.4 shows the dataflow path of the URL-based access control in a proxy cache. Comparing Fig. 6.4 with the dataflow path in a traditional proxy cache, it is seen that a URL access control module is inserted in the dataflow point 2 between the proxy and the web server.

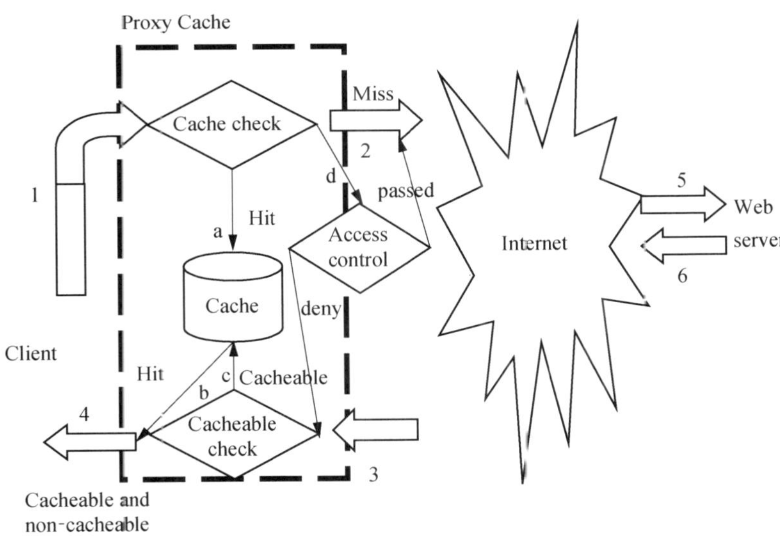

Fig. 6.4 URL-based access control at Stage 2 of AXform framework

Now let us look at the effect of the access control under various situations. After a new client request passes the dataflow point 1 of the proxy, the request will enter the cache check module. If it is a cache miss, the request will be forwarded to the access control module (depicted as arrow d). For a non-blocking URL request, it will be sent out along the dataflow path 2 as a normal request; the reply data will also be treated normally. On the other hand, if it is a forbidden URL, the proxy will send back a denied reply to the client. It is worth pointing out that the denied reply will go through the cacheable check module first and then to the dataflow point 4 before it reaches the client. The reason for doing this is to cache the denied reply (or the transformed request decision) in the proxy for possible future reuse.

A more interesting situation is when a cache hit due to a subsequent request to the same URL occurs. Since the transformation is done at Stage 2, cache hit to a client request will imply:

- No transformation is triggered for the current request.
- The client is served with the previously transformed request decision that is cached in the proxy.

This is what we call the reuse of transformation decision in proxy. And it is made possible through the hit in the proxy cache, assuming no change in the access control list. In terms of the performance consideration, access control is better carried out at Stage 2 of the framework than at Stage 1 because

- With an increasing size of the control list of forbidden URL addresses, the time for URL checking is both time and system resource consuming.
- The access control is assumed to be "universal", independent of the client and network information.

6.3.3 Stage 3 of AXform Framework: Server Data Stage

The server data stage of the AXform framework starts when the first data byte of a requested object reaches the proxy and ends when the proxy receives the last byte of the requested object. Possible transformation might take place on the reply data upon its arrival at the proxy. Note that caching of the reply object is done between Stage 3 and Stage 4 of the framework. Just like Stage 2, Stage 3 of the AXform will not be triggered in case of a valid proxy cache hit for the client's object request.

6.3.3.1 Input Data Availability and Output

At this stage, the proxy receives the reply data from the web server. Besides the information known at Stage 1 and Stage 2 of the framework, there are two types of new data available here. The first one is the reply data for the requested object. The second one is the attributes of the requested object, which include the last modified time, expire time, cache control, ..., etc. If the object is served from the upstream proxy, the caching status of the object there can also be known. Other TCP/IP information of the web server such as the server IP address is available in this stage. All these information appear in the header fields of the HTTP reply.

The output of content transformation on the reply data at this stage is an HTTP reply, which includes the full set of correct header information and a data body. Note that since the output from this stage goes through the cacheable check module, any inappropriate header information here might affect the cacheability property of the requested object. It might even cause error in data transfer. This is because the server data is streamed back to the proxy in a chunk-by-chunk manner and the reply header information comes before the reply data of the requested object.

6.3.3.2 Caching Issue

Stage 3 of the AXform framework takes place before the proxy's cacheable check module that stores the reply data of a requested object into the local cache. Hence, instead of the original data copy, it is the transformed copy of the requested object that will be stored in the proxy cache under the same "old" URL name. Since this process is totally transparent to the client, cache consistency might be a problem. If the proxy does not have ways to judge whether the cached, *transformed* copy of the object is the same as the one in the original web server, a client might receive outdated or incorrect information. This makes the caching issue an important design consideration for the Stage 3 transformation in the AXform framework. At the same time, however, caching the transformed copy of a requested object allows possible future reuse of the transformation result. This performance benefit will be important when the transformation process is very time and resource consuming.

6.3.3.3 Appropriateness of Content Transformation

Transformation at Stage 3 of the AXform framework focuses on the content adaptation of the requested object body and/or its associated HTTP reply header. Interestingly enough, most of the previous works on proxy-based content transformation are done at this stage.

To help access the appropriateness of a content transformation function at this stage, we need to understand the two basic requirements for content transformation to take place at Stage 3. The first requirement is the streaming nature of the web object transfer. Since the chunk-by-chunk data streaming mode is so critical to the performance of web content delivery (in particular, user perceived time), whole object buffering for transformation at Stage 3 should not be used.

The second requirement is related to the chance for the cached, transformed copy of the object body to be reused by multiple clients. Transformation of the reply body data should be done at Stage 3 and the transformed result is stored in the proxy cache only if its reuse frequency is expected to be high. Note that even with high object reuse frequency, if the transformation requirement of an object is changed every time it is accessed, it might not be more appropriate to perform the transformation at Stage 3. This is because the proxy cache space is wasted to keep the unusable transformed object data. Network bandwidth is also wasted to fetch the original copy of the object data from the web server to the proxy cache for transformation every time it is accessed. Instead, it might be good to keep the original copy of the object data in the proxy (as is suggested for Stage 4 transformation in Section 6.3.4).

A good sample transformation at Stage 3 of the AXform framework is the lossless data compression.

6.3.3.4 Case Study: Real-Time Streaming Compression

Here we use the compression proxy as an example to illustrate how content transformation should take place at Stage 3 of the AXform framework.

Lossless data compression is a commonly used technique to save the storage space of a computer system. With the "world-wide-wait" problem and the relatively more expensive network cost over computer hardware cost, attention is now being shifted to automatic web data compression for reduction in network bandwidth demand. Furthermore, as we explain in the previous chapter of this book, text-based HTML compression not only brings reduction in the downloading time of the page container object but also allows the embedded objects of the page to be retrieved earlier. Our performance study shows that significant improvement in page downloading time, with an average of about 20% can be objected. Figure 6.5 shows the dataflow of the real-time streaming compression proxy.

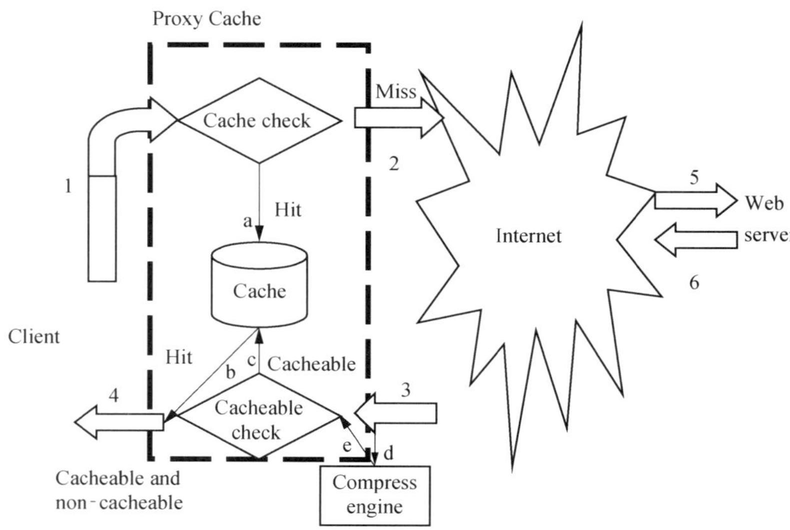

Fig. 6.5 Real-time lossless compression at Stage 3 of AXform framework

In this compression proxy, one compress engine module is deployed at Stage 3. When the body data of a requested object is sent to the proxy cache along the dataflow point 3, it will first pass through the compress engine before it is considered by the cacheable check module for possible storage in the proxy.

Due to the lossless nature of the compression, the compress engine will do a data type specific compression. In our implementation, zlib compression on the data chunks of text/HTML objects is performed. For objects of other content types (such as JPEG), no compression is performed. Zlib is used instead of the normal gzip because it allows data to be compressed in the streaming chunk by chunk manner. There is no need to buffer the whole object first before the transformation takes place. Furthermore, zlib is supported by current browsers such as IE 4+, Netscape 4.01+, and even IE for WinCE. Thus, the client need not install any decompression software or plug-in. Note that since the object body is changed, certain pre-adjustment to the information in the HTTP reply header fields needs to be done by the compress engine. Finally, to make the whole system robust, modification is done to the cache check and cacheable check modules so that "ancient" browsers will not be mishandled.

In this particular example, caching the compressed version of web objects in the proxy is a good design choice because there is only one transformed version of an object that is likely to be needed by all clients. Through caching, the performance cost of compression is greatly reduced.

6.3.4 Stage 4 of AXform Framework: Client Data Stage

The client data stage of the AXform framework starts when the data of a requested object is ready to be sent back to the client and ends when the proxy sends out the last byte of the requested object. Possible transformation might take place on the reply data as it is sent out to a client. Note that caching of the reply object (if any) is done before the starting of Stage 4.

6.3.4.1 Input Data Availability and Output

At this stage, the proxy sends the data of the requested object back to a client. This is the last hop of the entire retrieval datapath.

Just like the situation of Stage 1 and Stage 2, the key difference between the data availability of Stage 3 and Stage 4 for transformation is related to the information from the cacheable check module. All other information, including the header and the body of the requested object, upstream server's TCP/IP information, and other information available at Stage 1 and Stage 2, are available to both Stage 3 and Stage 4. This is expected because as the request and reply of an object flow along the four stages sequentially, information at a given stage is cumulated from its previous stages.

One special situation worth mentioning here is when the requested object is served from the local proxy cache. Since the entire object is available from the local proxy cache, greater flexibility can be given to the design of transformation function in this Stage 4.

The output data from the transformation module at this stage should be a full HTTP reply to the client. It should have the correct and complete header and body; data must also be delivered in a streaming way. If possible, the output can carry hints for the client to understand that the delivered object is a transformed one.

6.3.4.2 Caching Issue

Transformation at Stage 4 of the AXform framework is done after the cache. Thus it is not affected by any outcome of the proxy cache. For this situation to occur, the proxy cache is likely to keep the original copy of the requested object instead of the previously transformed copies. Every time an object is requested, it will pass through Stage 4 transformation engine for content modification. There is no reuse of the transformed data (but data reuse is possible for the original data copy in the proxy cache).

6.3.4.3 Appropriateness of Content Transformation

Similar to Stage 3, transformation at Stage 4 of the AXform framework focuses on the adaptation of reply header and body content. Since this is the last hop in the whole delivery procedure, it is the ideal place for client adaptation to take place on the requested web object body.

One good example of using Stage 4 transformation is the adaptive transcoding that has been mentioned in many other researchers' work. Surprisingly, most of them suggest to cache the transformed copy of the image objects in the proxy. In terms of our AXform framework, it means Stage 3 transformation. We hold quite different viewpoints and argue for Stage 4 transformation. Almost all adaptive transcoding technologies are lossy.

If the adaptation is done at Stage 3, the cached copy of the requested object is not likely to be reused. This is due to the large number of possible adaptation options to best fit the wide variations of client demand. As a result, both the cache space and the network bandwidth will be wasted. However, if the adaptation is done at Stage 4, the proxy cache will hold the original copy of the object. Thus based on different client information, appropriate lossy transcoding can be applied to the cached object easily without the need to fetch it from the original web server.

6.3.4.4 Case Study: Local Advertisement Uploading Based on Client's DNS/IP

To help understand the client data stage (or Stage 4) of the AXform framework, the local advertisement uploading based on client's DNS/IP is given below.

Online advertisement is one of the major financial driving forces for the Internet movement. With localizing content for the advertisement, its effect will be improved significantly. The concept of local advertisement has been widely accepted by web content providers today. The local advertisement uploading proxy is developed to solve this problem. Figure 6.6 shows the dataflow of the proxy with local advertisement uploading based on client's DNS/IP.

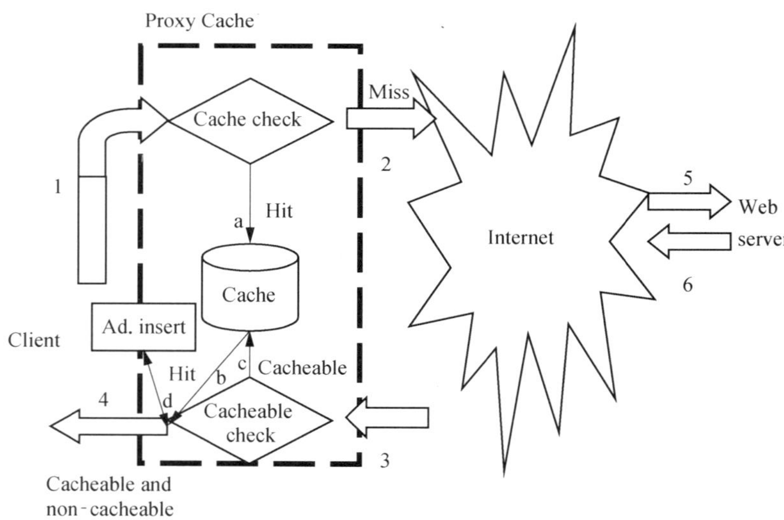

Fig. 6.6 Local advertisement uploading based on client DNS/IP at Stage 4 of AXform framework

In this local advertisement proxy, an advertisement module, called the Ad. Insert module, is deployed on top of the proxy cache. When an object is ready to be delivered to a client at dataflow point 4, it will first be passed to the Ad. Insert module (depicted as arrow d). This module will then do the local advertisement uploading based on some predefine rules. Given the requested page URL and the client DNS/IP information, the module will either insert a new advertisement into the requested web page or replace the original advertisement with a localized copy. For example, for a web surfer from the education sector, one extra banner about the local education exhibition will be inserted in the Yahoo education page. It is also worth mentioning there that the HTTP reply header also need to be adjusted since the object body is changed.

6.3.5 Summary

To perform content transformation in proxy, there are four possible stages where the transformers can be deployed. They are the client request stage, server request stage, server data stage, and client data stage. These four stages represent different points where the request and reply data go into or come out of a proxy server.

Depending on the input data availability and the output data, we can divide them into two categories, the request stage and the data stage. Stage 1 and Stage 2 belong to the request stages. At these two stages, the only data available are the request information and the client information. Thus transformation at these stages can only adapt the request, performing tasks such as redirect, access control, anonymous request, etc. The difference between Stage 1 and Stage 2 is the caching issue and the reuse of previously transformed decisions. Stage 1 is before the cache check module. It needs not worry about the cached copy and is good for personalization. Stage 2 is after the cache check module. It can enjoy the reuse of previously transformed decisions and will be bypassed in case of the cache hit situation.

Stage 3 and Stage 4 are the data stages. At these stages, the reply data are available to the proxy, thus allowing more transformation functions to be done. Most of the transformations are likely to be content-based. The difference between Stage 3 and Stage 4 is also the caching issue and the reuse of previcusly transformed content. Stage 3 usually keeps the transformed copy of the object in cache whereas Stage 4 transformation prefers to cache the original copy of the object. One important thing about Stage 3 and Stage 4 transformation is that the HTTP reply header needs to be adjusted when content transformation is done in these stages. Table 6.1 summarizes the characteristics of the four stages of the AXform framework.

Table 6.1 Summary of Characteristics of the Four Stages of the AXform Framework

	Stage 1	Stage 2	Stage 3	Stage 4
Input Data availability	Request info.	Request info.	Reply data, accumulatively	Reply data, accumulatively
Output data	Client request	Server request	Server data	Client data
Requirements for transformers	Low overhead, no reuse of transformation result	Reuse of transformation result	Streaming, reuse of transformation result	Streaming, no reuse of transformation result
Sample transformation	Client IP/DNS based redirect	ACL, request filtering	Compression, content filtering	Client Adaptation

Finally, for practical content transformation proxy, one adaptation function might need operations and the information from more than one stage of the AXform framework. However, the guideline of designing transformations at different stages is still the same as what is described in this section.

6.4 System Implementation Considerations for AXform Framework

In the last section, we propose the four stages of the AXform framework. Now we would like to discuss its system implementation considerations. From our experience of building such active proxy systems, we find out that there are several important general issues that are shared among them. These include the creation and handling of the working space, collection of the client information, performing appropriate modification to request and reply, and sometimes even modifying the cache control module of the proxy. In the rest of the chapter, each of them will be discussed in detail.

6.4.1 Handling of Working Space

The very first step of any content transformation in the proxy is to create and manage the working space. The working space here refers to the whole set of resources that can be used during the process of the content transformation. For any kind of transformation to take place, such working space needs to be created at the very beginning of the process and is carefully managed until its end. Below are some usual considerations of the working space.

6.4.1.1 Global and Local Space, Permanent and Temporary Space

Just as what happens in any computer system, the first thing needed is the space to store data. As we describe before, object is transmitted through the network in a chunk-by-chunk, streaming manner. And during the whole object retrieval process, there are four stages from the viewpoint of a proxy cache. Hence, we further divide the space into different categories. For space that is used by every data chunk, we call it permanent space. For space that is used by one chunk, we call it temporary space. For space that is used in more than one stage, we call it global space. And for space that is used only in one stage, we call it local space. To describe it more clearly, Table 6.2 gives all the possible situations of the space usage:

Table 6.2 Possible Situations of Space Usage

	Global	Local
Permanent	A	B
Temporary	C	D

For all these spaces, the basic requirement is that they should belong to only one transaction or retrieval and they should not affect the spaces that belong to another transaction. Therefore they are better created within the data structure of each transaction. However, for different spaces, they have very different properties. And, the creation and usage of such spaces can be very different.

For type A, it is the permanent global space. Such data is used throughout the entire object transmission process in more than one stage. One example is the client information such as the browser type and the client's preference. In the system implementation, we need to create a global data entry for this kind of space at Stage 1 for each request. Then, during the subsequent stages, the system can assign values or reference data from this space easily.

For type B, it is the permanent local space. Such space is always used in one stage by all data chunks passing through it. One typical usage is for the buffering of data chunks during the transmission. In some transformation, we need the data that might exist in more than one chunk. A good example is the language translation, where we need complete words or even sentences to be the input to the translator. If we do the translation at Stage 3, we need a permanent local space to buffer partial words or sentences. This is because there is always a chance for such word or sentence to cross over two chunks. For this kind of data space, we only need to create it once at the first time when the stage that needs this is reached. The value in the space will be modified and referenced only at that given stage. At other stages, this space is totally unreachable. This is especially important for some security sensitive applications. For example, a user password is better stored in the type B space in Stage 2 than in the type A space.

For type C, it is the temporary global space. Such data space is used by one chunk in more than one stage. A case in point is the buffer for the first chunk of the reply data. This kind of buffer is extremely useful when we do the HTTP reply header modification. Typically, the HTTP reply header sent back by a web server is in one single chunk. To modify the reply header only, we just need a type C space to buffer the header at Stage 3 or Stage 4 for the first reply data chunk. For such type C space, the system creates it as a global space at the point when it is needed. The value in the space can be modified and referenced at any of the four stages. This space needs to be released back to the system once it is no longer in use.

For type D, it is the temporary local space. Such data space is used by one chunk in one stage only. A typical example is the space to hold the temporary variables such as registers and counters that we declare and use during the transformation process. For this type of space, it is created as a temporary variable by the system at any stage and it is only used in that stage once. After the chunk is passed to the next network level, the space is released back to the system.

One thing we need to point out here is that the global and permanent space always occupies more system resource than the local and temporary space. Hence, when we design the system architecture, the global and permanent space is used only when it is absolutely necessary. This is important because the proxy is always under high workload. Moreover, all these spaces need to be released back to the system as soon as they are no longer in use. This topic will be discussed in detail in 6.4.1.3.

6.4.1.2 Temp File

One typical working space is the temporary file. Very often, we need to open a temp file to record information. This is particularly true if the content transformation is done in a whole file dump manner.

There are a few things that handling temp file needs to pay more attention to. The first one is related to the creation of temp file. In the system implementation, it is possible to create temp file at any stage. Usually, it is created at Stage 3 as the buffer space for the incoming reply data. To open the file, we need to interact with the system's file system.

Generally speaking, there are three concerns for opening a file. They are the file name, authority, and system file descriptors. When a file is opened, a unique file name is assigned to it. Then in the later data manipulation in the file, the name should be easily referenced by the system. In a typical proxy system, such a file is usually designed inside a multiple-levels directory. By hashing the request, the file opened will be assigned one unique path and one unique filename. With the hashing function, it is also easy for the proxy cache to find out the temp file. For our content transformation, each temp file is related to one particular transaction. Thus the hashing or similar indexing technology can be used to assign the file name.

After the file is opened, the next concern is the authority. As we know, the proxy is supposed to serve lots of clients. At any given moment, it is likely to have more than one transaction. Therefore we need to have a mechanism to assure the authority of a temp file. This means that the temp file opened by one transaction can not be written by any other transactions. After the file is created, we need to read or write the file. Since this can happen at any stage, the data structure needs to remember that the file should be a global one.

To optimize the read and write operation of the file, some kind of memory buffering, synchronized write technology might be used here. Since the proxy handles multiple transactions at one time, it is possible that a lot of temporary files are open concurrently. In any operating system, there is always a limitation to the number of opened file descriptors. So in the system design, we need to make sure that we do not run out of file descriptors. One way of solving this problem is to free the file descriptor as soon as it is no longer in use. Again, this will be discussed in more detail in 6.4.1.3.

6.4.1.3 Garbage Collection

As it is defined, the space is used in the whole process of transformation. Therefore quite a lot of system resources are used for creating and referencing them. Since the proxy needs to have a high performance, these resources must be used efficiently. In case of running out of the resources, all the spaces that are no longer in use must be collected back by the system. For the four types of spaces described previously, due to their different usages, their collection mechanisms are different. For the permanent space such as type A and type B, it is created and used throughout the whole data transfer process of the object. Its collection can only be done when the last object chunk is sent to a client. For the temporary space like type C and type D, it is only used by a particular chunk during the data transfer. Thus, they will be freed once the chunk is sent back to the client.

For a temp file, it is a bit complicated. Usually, a temp file is to record the information throughout the entire object transfer. Thus the system is only able to collect back the file descriptors once the transfer is finished. Such file needs to be deleted to release the name resource back to the system's hashing table and to free up the disk space as well. We discuss the temp file as a special case here because we also need to consider the sudden crash and restart of the system. In real-life environment, the proxy system should be fault tolerant. From our experience with the transcoding proxies, we must build a special module to handle such sudden restart in order to avoid the mess in the file system.

6.4.1.4 New Process

To do transformation such as transcoding, the ideal architecture is to deploy the transcoder into the proxy system. That means by integrating the transcoder and the proxy together, we get a new proxy system. And the transcoding is just a function in the proxy. However, this is not always the case. A transcoder is not always easy to be integrated with the proxy. Furthermore, for the 100% availability concern of the proxy server, sometimes it might be better to deploy the transcoder as a standalone engine. In this case, the proxy needs to create a new process when it wants to trigger the transcoder. From the viewpoint of the system implementation, starting a new process definitely consumes certain system resource and has some overhead. For the resource requirement, there is not much that one can do or avoid. The best we can do is to start a new process only if it is absolutely necessary. For the overhead, we could find a way to "hide" it if it is done properly. The "magic" here is the time and the manner the process is created. As we know, the object is transmitted in chunk sequence and the proxy acts as an intermediary to rally the chunk streaming. For each chunk, if the process is not necessary before the sending out of the chunk, we can start the process only after the sending of data begins. By doing this, we have the chance of hiding the overhead of starting the process and even the overhead of the process itself. For better performance, we can further assign less CPU cycles for unimportant processes.

6.4.2 Accessing Other System Resources

During the content transformation, we may need to access other system resources such as database and socket. This is another kind of resources required. In some transformation such as local advertisement uploading or content filtering, there will have a lot of rules and URL libraries. During the transformation process, the querying and updating of these libraries are very common. To achieve a higher performance, it is better to deploy database technology here rather than to use simple flat file operations. Hence in the system design, we need to give the authority of using the database service provided by the operating system applications.

Other system resources such as the socket might also be used. It is possible that during the transformation process, transforming proxy needs to communicate with other servers. This is particularly true if the I-CAP approach [ICAPa] is used. Under the I-CAP implementation, the proxy that receives the data will communicate with the ICAP server for a given transformation to be done there. Thus in developing such a transformation system, it is necessary to assure that such environment system resources are available to the transformation system.

6.4.3 Client Information Collection

Collection of client information is important for adaptive delivery. This is because clients can vary a lot with their network, hardware and software configuration. Thus we need to differentiate them according to the their configuration. The more a client can be understood, the better he can be served. Generally speaking, the client information of interest includes his ID information, his software and hardware information, his personal preference, and his network information. Since different clients might have different preferences towards the same content object, client information is important to quality-based adaptive content delivery. This information collection is usually done at Stage 1 and the result is stored in a global permanent space.

6.4.3.1 Client ID Information

The client ID information includes a client machine's IP address, DNS name, socket bound between a client and a proxy, client's user ID/password if the authentication is used in the proxy, client's email address if the client software sends out such information, etc. All these information are necessary to understand where the request comes from and who the user is. Usually, the IP address and the DNS name give ideas about which group the client belongs to (such as whether he is on academic LAN, in commercial company, or from the ISP's dialup modem pool). The socket number further differentiates different sessions for the same client.

To know exactly who the client is, the most important piece of information comes from the user ID when the proxy authentication is used. About the client ID, one thing that we need to point out is that in proxy transformation, the only client IDs that the proxy can understand are those from the authenticated users. Furthermore, such authentication is done in a hop-by-hop manner, which means that a given proxy only knows its own clients' IDs and not the IDs of its child proxy's. Some browsers send out the browser register information such as the owner's email address and company name when the anonymous web visit option is turned off. Such information may be used as a hint for the identification of a web visitor.

6.4.3.2 Client Software and Hardware Information

To understand a client better, we need to know who the client is, where he is from and what kind of hardware and software he is using. Such information is extremely useful when client adaptation of web content is needed. At Stage 1, upon receiving an HTTP request from a client, such information can possibly be retrieved from the HTTP request header. Most of the information usually come from the agent information that is included in the header. From the agent information, one can easily find out: 1) what kind of browser software a client uses, like Netscape or Internet Explorer, 2) the version of the browser, and 3) the operating system, like Windows 95, Windows NT, Windows CE or any kind of Unix. Generally speaking, there is no direct information about the hardware configuration. But with the agent information, we can still get hints about that. For example, if a client's agent information indicates that he is using an Internet Explorer 3.0 of low resolution and the operating system is Windows CE, one can draw the conclusion that he is using some kind of slim devices like the pocket PC.

6.4.3.3 Client Preference

With the content negotiation defined by the HTTP/1.1, modern browsers begin to include the client preferences in the request header. Though this is still far from complete as compared to the numerous possibilities of content negotiation mentioned in the HTTP/1.1, it already gives the proxy system a lot of information about the ability of the browser and the preferences of the client. Most of the information comes from the Accept header. With the Accept header, an HTTP request can specify exactly what kind of information the browser can deal with and which version it prefers. A good example is the multilingual web page in WWW. The browser understands what kind of language the client wants, usually at the time of installation when the client sets the language choice. Then, later in the request of a web page, it might send out the request with the Accept-language header indicating the preferred specific language encoding. Such information will be interpreted by the server that supports such multilingual content negotiation and the web page of that language will be sent to the client. Another example is to do automatic compression in the network. Since not all browsers support the (de)compression and different browsers might even support different compression algorithms, it is necessary for the compression system to understand whether the client can accept and understand the compressed data. This information can be obtained from the Accept-Encoding header.

6.4.3.4 Client Network Information

Another piece of useful data is the information of the network that a client uses. In real life, the network speed varies so much that it is important to differentiate the clients using the high speed network and those using the dial up network. Generally speaking, it is quite hard to get this information from the HTTP request header. Nevertheless, we can get hints about this information from the client's IP address, DNS, and the hardware/software configuration. The client's IP address would suggest where he is from. The DNS can sometimes give more information, such as if he is from the education sector or from the commercial network. From the DNS, we can even know if he uses a modem dial up or a ADSL. Together with the information of the hardware and software configuration, other hints about the network condition can be obtained. For example, the pocket PC is likely to use a wireless modem to dial up. Note that at the stage of client information collection, the client network information can not be 100% known. Such information might be further obtained in the environment parameters collection phase.

6.4.4 Server Information Collection

Like the collection of the client information, we also need to collect the server information. Understanding the server ability is critical if the proxy wants to negotiate with the web server. And some server information such as the server time and caching information might give great hints on the performance of the delivery system. The server information usually resides in the HTTP reply header. Some examples are server's identification, server software information and some others. Such collection is usually done at Stage 3.

6.4.4.1 Server ID

The server identification here refers to the DNS and IP of the replying server. This may be different from the one defined in the client's request header if the redirection technology is used. This is the most accurate information about the actual server who answers the HTTP request. Just like the client ID, this server ID can give hints about where the server is, what organization it belongs to and even, sometimes, what network it sits on.

6.4.4.2 Software

Server software information is very important for us to understand the web server. Like the client's hardware and software information, the server software gives out most of these information. The first piece of information is the server software and version such as Apache 1.3 or IIS. The second piece of information is the operation system (e.g. UNIX vs. Windows). The third piece of information is the supported packages. For example, besides the standard web server package, the apache server has a lot of optional packages such as SSL, perl, PHP, etc. This information is important to understand the ability of the web server.

6.4.4.3 Others

There are some other information worth mentioning here. One is the protocol used. An HTTP request made to a server can ask for HTTP/1.1 or HTTP/1.0. However, which protocol to be used is the decision of the server. And at the very beginning of the reply, the server will announce what protocol it uses. With this information, one can know whether the advanced features defined in HTTP 1.1 can be asked from the server. Another piece of data is the information filled by the upstream server. If the working system does not access the web server directly, there will be an upstream server trying to fill the Via header in the reply. Such information gives great hints on whether the object is cacheable and some rough ideas about the fresh lifetime of the object.

6.4.5 Environment Parameters Collection

The system environment parameters are important for the proxy to understand its dynamic operating situation. Here we want to focus on two groups of environment parameters, the network environment parameters and the system resource usage. This parameter collection procedure is a dynamic one and it is done throughout the object delivery process.

6.4.5.1 Network Environment

The transformation system we propose is to be used as a proxy in the network. For content adaptation, it is done mainly because of the wide variations of network, hardware and software. The hardware and software information is fixed once it is known. However, the network environment keeps changing. As we said before, a system can get hints about the network situation from other information sources. However, to get accurate information, a standalone module that does the monitoring of the network needs to be deployed. This module periodically collects the network status data for the reference of the system.

6.4.5.2 System Resource Usage

In a practical system, the system resource should be managed properly to make sure that the system would not hang up due to the draining up of resource. The system resource includes the storage space, memory space, file descriptors, sockets, active process number, etc. As we mention that during the transformation, the transformation module might need to open files, open sockets, and even create processes. If we do not have a feasible way of managing the resource usage, the system might run out of them easily. Practically, we need to set up some macro limits for the usage of these resources and abide by such limits throughout the whole process of the object delivery.

6.4.6 Client Request Modification

The first possible transformation occurs at Stage 1 or Stage 2, which tries to modify the client request. A client request usually has a header only, except for the POST method. Thus the modification of a client request mainly focuses on the request header information. We modify a client request because we want to pass certain information to the web server. For example, there is a JPEG2000 image with the size of 100 K. A slow client just wants to see the tailored version of the image, thus he issues a request of the first 10 K using the range option. However, the proxy cache might already have the first 5 K in it. Therefore, the proxy delivers the first 5 K to the client first. In the mean time, it rewrites the range request to a 5~10 K one and sends it to the server. Following this example, it is easy to understand why any system implementation of prefetching upon partial hit needs to modify the client request. One important thing worth mentioning here is the consistency of the client information and the modified client requests. Of course, one should maintain the consistency of these two as much as possible. However, for some particular reasons such as system simplicity, we might sometimes break the consistency. All these depend on the requirements of the system implementation.

6.4.7 HTTP Reply Header Modification

Most of the transformations are done to the body data of an HTTP reply. Since the HTTP header is a kind of metadata for the HTTP body, it is likely that the HTTP reply header needs to be modified. It is possible to modify any header information in the transformation process. We will discuss some of the most common ones below.

6.4.7.1 Content Length

A web server uses the content length to tell a client how long an object is. With this information, a client can know when the retrieval process is done. Though there are other methods for the server to notify the client about the completion of the transfer process (such as the "empty chunk"), the content length is still the most widely used method. Inconsistency between the content length specified in the header and the actual content length of the body might generate errors in the object delivery and caching. Thus the transformation system should try its best to fill in the correct content length in the modified header. However, according to today's HTTP protocol, the HTTP header containing the content length information is at the very beginning of the HTTP reply. In other words, the header comes before the body. As we discussed earlier, for performance reasons, chunk-streaming mode is preferred over object-buffering mode for the content transformation. This creates difficulty when filling in the correct content length information in the header. For some special kind of transformation, it might be possible to predict the length of the transformed copy. But in the general case, we need to use other methods to notify the client about the ending of the retrieval.

6.4.7.2 Content Encoding

The content encoding header specifies the encoding technology of the HTTP body. For a given transcoding technology applied to the transformation system, the content encoding field needs to be modified. The modification is actually quite easy. It should be noted that once this header is changed, the length of the whole HTTP header needs to be adjusted, too.

6.4.7.3 Cache Related Information

Since we are focusing on the content transformation in the proxy, the system developed should try to take the advantages of the proxy caching. In the HTTP protocol, to assure the freshness of the cached data, besides the definition of cacheable and non-cacheable option, the protocol also defines a cache control header to help the web server control the distribution of its document. Other cache related headers include the Last-modified-time, Expire, Content length, etc. It is suggested that the proxy should just follow the header to do the caching. However, we found that very often, such header information is not well set. Sometimes, the proxy might have a better idea of how this object should be cached and revalidated. This is especially true in the transformation system, where the proxy understands the properties of the transformed objects much better than the original server. Thus it might be acceptable for the transformation system to overwrite such header when it is found necessary. Another approach is to modify the cache related modules in the proxy. This will be discussed later in Section 6.4.9.1.

The modification of the HTTP reply header can be done at Stage 3 or Stage 4. Their difference is on what HTTP reply header will be stored in the proxy's caching system. For modifications made at Stage 3, it will affect the cached copy and client's copy. For modifications made at Stage 4, it will only affect the client's copy.

6.4.8 HTTP Body Modification

An HTTP body is actually what the client requests for. And most transformations are applied to the HTTP body. We have discussed a lot in this book about how transformation on the reply body data should be done in order to achieve high performance. Here we are not going to repeat. Instead, we would like to raise some issues that need to be handled carefully during system implementation.

6.4.8.1 Buffer Overflow

In the implementation of transformation proxy, the buffer is widely used as a temporary memory storage for the information. In the practical environment, the problem of buffer overflow is a common one. There are usually two reasons for this to occur. The first one is the exception during the transformation. One example is in the decompression proxy. Sometimes we might deploy two proxies in the content distributed network, one for compression and the other for decompression. For decompression, it is quite hard to predict the expansion ratio of the compressed data. Even if a system allocates a very big memory buffer, it still can not totally expurgate the possibility of the buffer overflow. Another reason is the handling of the working space. If the working space is not carefully handled (e.g. garbage not collected in time or working space confused up among transactions), the buffer overflow problem will occur occasionally.

6.4.8.2 Hiding Overhead

The modification of the HTTP body is the most resource consuming part. It is inevitable that certain overhead will be introduced. But with careful system implementation, one can try to "hide" the overhead. As we mention before, the object transfer in the network is in the chunk streaming mode. And a proxy is the rally point between a client and a server. Thus in actual system implementation, the transformation should not change the chunk streaming nature of data transfer unless it is absolutely necessary. For example, the logging and analyzing of an object during its transfer is quite common in the transformation system. Such processes should not be triggered before the delivery of the chunk. Actually, by triggering such process after the chunk delivery begins, the overhead will almost be fully hidden. Similar method can be used to hide the overhead of reading and writing the file system.

6.4.9 Cache Related Module

In developing the transformation proxy, it is better to make the transformer modular. Hence, one should avoid modifying the working mechanism of the original proxy cache as much as possible. However, to further utilize the cache system provided by the proxy, we might need to make some modification to the cache related module. There are two kinds of such cache related modules, one for the cache control module and the other for the cache hit/miss check module. Each of these modules will be discussed below.

6.4.9.1 Cache Control Module

The cache control module is used by the proxy cache to determine whether the HTTP reply is cacheable. It is triggered between Stage 3 and Stage 4. As we discussed in the modification of HTTP header, the transformation proxy might sometimes need to overwrite the rules set by the original server for better caching. This can be done by modifying the HTTP reply header. But this solution might have undesirable side effects. With the cache control header modified, all the clients and the downstream proxies will get the revised cache control information. There is no way for them to differentiate whether this rule is set by the original server or by the transformation system. This might affect the caches of the clients and downstream proxies. An alternate solution is to modify the cache control module. By applying new rules to the cache control module, we can control the cache management of this working system and at the same time limit the effect to this system only. For this solution, we need to know the side effect of deploying new rules and make sure it will not malfunction.

6.4.9.2 Cache Hit/Miss Module

The cache hit/miss check module is used to determine whether the request can be served from the local cache or it needs to consult the original server. This module includes the function of sending validation check (IMS) to the original server when the proxy cache is not sure about the freshness of the cached data. Very often, this module is used between Stage 1 and Stage 2. The rules to determine whether the request is a hit or a miss are usually set by the protocol. Different proxy caching softwares might make some minor changes to optimize the performance. However, in the transformation system design, these rules may be changed quite a lot. The transformation system needs to modify the caching rules to assure the availability and performance of the whole system, especially when the transformed copy is stored in the proxy cache. To explain this in detail, let's take the compression proxy as an example. In the compression proxy, the compression itself costs quite a lot of system resource and almost every modern browser can interpret the compressed data correctly. Therefore, it is better to cache the compressed data in the proxy cache for reuse. Yet as a working proxy system, it also needs to serve the "ancient" browser. If a request from such browser comes and the requested object is in cache, the original cache hit/miss module will be considered as a hit. But the problem is that delivering the cached copy to this old browser is not correct! In this case, the cache hit/miss module needs to be revised to make sure that such requests will go back to the original server directly.

6.5 Conclusion

In this chapter, we propose a 4-stage AXform framework as a systematic way of understanding how, when, and where a given transformation function should be performed in the proxy cache. Basically, the selection choice is often related to the possibility of reusing the transformed content decision and data. In the second part of this chapter, we discuss the design considerations for implementating a transformation proxy server in detail. Various design guidelines are also given. In the next chapter, we are going to apply these guidelines to a real case study of proxy-based automatic watermarking system.

Reference

(SQUID 2010) Squid Web Proxy Cache. http: //www.squid-cache.org. Accessed 14 April 2010

7

Conclusion

7.1 Conclusion of the Book

The rapid growth of the Internet has made itself more and more heterogeneous. Users vary a lot in their hardware, software and network condition. To make the situation more complicated, they want more content personalization and customization. This makes the "good-service" content delivery no longer a simple concept. Download speed of a web page is still a basic requirement, on top of which best-fit content delivery, content access control and policy enforcement are also required. Each solution on web server or client browser has its limitations. Researchers today are seeking solutions on web intermediary servers. Active web intermediaries were first defined in active network. Now it is adopted into content delivery framework to provide good quality services. So far there have been some transformation proxy servers such as Pythia and TranSend. Industry is also pushing protocols which include I-CAP, SOAP and OPES. However, we believe that there are some fundamental issues that need to be addressed. In this book, we proposed several models for better understanding and developing of such active web intermediaries. Together we presented the actual system framework and design considerations for the implementation.

7.1.1 Performance Model

Speed is always a key concern in web content delivery. And it is one of the most important performance indicators for any kind of network services. The traditional way of evaluating the speed is by measuring the object retrieval time. However, we argue that it is not sufficient to evaluate the performance of web content delivery. There are two reasons for this. The first reason is that, when a user sends out a request, the web page he is expecting is often composed of multiple objects. He may not be aware of this since it is done automatically by the browser. But to a user, what matters is the delay to download the full page. Unfortunately, the download speed of each individual object may not reflect the download speed of the whole page. The second reason, which is more important, is that there exist dependencies among objects within the web page. The dependencies we mention here is the delivery dependency. This kind of dependency makes the traditional object based performance model difficult to evaluate the web content delivery.

In Chapter 3, we proposed a novel chunk-level latency dependence model (C-LDM) to illustrate how the objects inside one web page are dependent on each other in today's content delivery mechanism and how the network delay of each object affects the total page downloading time. In this model, we chose chunk as the basic level since in web content delivery, the basic data unit is a chunk (as defined in HTTP). We broke down the whole retrieval process of a web page into chunk sequences of different objects. By researching the dependencies of different chunks of different objects, we found out the dependencies between embedded objects exist for almost all web pages. We further broke the embedded object retrieval time into object definition time, object queuing time, connection time and chunk transmission time. By studying the details of all these delays incurred during one web transaction, we found out that the dependency between the basic web page template (e.g. HTML object of the page) and the embedded objects is a major factor that determines the total web page download delay. In some specific network environment, this dependency can be the dominant factor for the downloading delay. This knowledge is valuable. On the one hand, it provides the knowledge of how to evaluate the web content delivery service. On the other hand, it gives us hints on where the delay comes from and how we can efficiently reduce it.

7.1.2 Improving the Delivery by Reducing the Object Dependence

Based on the knowledge we got from the C-LDM, we proposed two ways to reduce the object dependency in web page retrieval in Chapter 4 so that the overall page retrieval delay can be reduced.

The first method is called Object Declaration. In cooperation with content developer, it is possible to declare the embedded objects at the beginning of their container template (e.g. HTML) for the web page. In this way, the dependency between the embedded objects and the basic template is reduced. The client can know what the embedded objects in a web page are at the first few chunks of the basic template. This reduces the object definition time and achieves a kind of "push forward" effect. We used the real-life web traffic traces to simulate Object Declaration. We found out that the improvement is quite obvious. With the performance improvement ranging from 3% to 12%, this method has promising effect on reducing the page download latency. The disadvantage of this method is that the object declaration part might be too large. Thus we suggested that the number of the objects to be declared could be adapted to the network parameters such as the number of parallel connections.

The second method is Page Structure Table (PST). With this method, the proxy as a web intermediary server will record the page structure. Therefore, when the page is retrieved next time, the proxy will know the page structure immediately upon the time it gets the request (in case of cache hit). Therefore the dependency between embedded objects and their basic template is reduced and the resulting page retrieval time is decreased. The advantage of this method is that it is transparent to the client and the web server. However, since the hit ratio of a proxy cache is usually not high, the actual benefit of the method in real life is not as high as that of the Object Declaration method. The simulation showed that the benefit of PST is around 1% to 4%.

These two methods compliment to each other. The simulation showed that by integrating these two methods, the page downloading time can be decreased by 3% to 18%, which is quite significant.

7.1.3 Transformation Model

Content transformation is the core concept of active web intermediaries. Due to the streaming feature of the network, different transformation methods have different impact on network performance. In Chapter 5, we did a detailed analysis of the network transformation and its implications to performance.

First, we defined a general model for real-time content transformation. From the viewpoint of network transmission, we classified the transformation applications into byte streaming, chunk streaming and file buffering. Due to network streaming transmission requirement, we studied the performance impact of streaming and buffering transformation mode. In web content delivery, where HTTP is the most popular protocol, since data is streamed from servers to clients chunk by chunk, we further differentiated transformation under byte streaming and chunk streaming. Different parameter combinations in the transformation model could be mapped into these three modes. Next, we studied the performance impact of these three modes. We introduced the C-LDG (chunk level dependence graph) to analyze the impact of the different modes. We found that although almost all of the transformations could be done in the buffering mode, this mode will introduce node-splitting, regrouping, and push-backward in the C-LDG. These three effects introduce significant delay in web page retrieval. Comparatively, the overhead in byte streaming and chunk streaming modes are relatively small. Taking practicality into consideration, chunk streaming is ideal for real-time content transformation in web intermediary servers. Referring to the mapping between the transformation model and the three transformation modes, useful hints can be obtained on how the transformation engine should be designed in web intermediaries.

7.1.4 System Framework and Requirements

In Chapter 6, we presented the system framework and requirements for such active web intermediary services. We focused on the design and implementation considerations of such system architecture.

First, we proposed a 4-stage AXForm framework for web intermediaries. A typical web transaction going through a web intermediary was broken down into, client request stage, server request stage, server data stage and client data stage. Each stage has its unique properties in data availability, input and output. For this system framework, we wanted to combine it with the basic caching function in traditional web proxy, since it has been proven to be an efficient way of reducing download delay and bandwidth consumption. Thus we emphasized a lot on the relationship between each of the four stages and the basic cache function in the proxy. What will be put in the cache? What will happen for a cache hit and cache miss? What will be reused, cached original object, cached transformed object, or both? Questions like this were well answered in Chapter 6.

After defining this system framework, we discussed the system requirements for such active web intermediaries. To implement such a system, besides a scalable system framework, we also need detailed knowledge on system requirements. Generally speaking, the following things need to be carefully handled. The first one is the working space. All the transformation applications need a space to run, in memory, swap or on hard disk. And these spaces need to be managed efficiently. The system also needs to have the freedom to generate new processes and to collect client, server and environment information. Finally, in order to fulfill the purpose of transformation, the system also needs to have the authority to manipulate the client request and server reply. Of course this manipulation will be done according to the popular protocol which both the client and the server understand and agree. All these system requirements were discussed in detail in Chapter 6.

7.2 Future Research

In the coming future, we can expect the Internet to be a major media of our daily life. Therefore, the requirements of high quality content delivery will never end. With active web intermediary servers to be accepted as an efficient way to provide good quality service for content delivery, there are still open topics to be researched.

7.2.1 APIs Definition

It is a good approach to make the basic framework for active web intermediaries scalable by defining a set of generic APIs for any third party to "plug" in their applications. Once this is done, the research in this area can be further divided into basic framework research and application "soft chip" development.

7.2.2 Unified Data Format

The purpose of active web intermediaries is to provide good content delivery service. With the help of other technologies such as the multimedia data format, this goal can be achieved better. Data format is widely used in the web today to achieve different goals in content delivery. Image data format like JPEG 2000 is proposed for a better image compress ratio. Its layered property is also good for better data reuse. Markup language format like ESI is proposed to decompose one object into different segments since each of them might have different properties such as TTL or ownership. It will be of great research interest to combine all these data formats into one. This new data format must meet the different requirements of high reuse, easy decomposition and combination, and scalable transmission.

7.2.3 Data Integrity and Security

Once the transformation in network is accepted, data integrity and security will emerge as an important concern. How can one be sure that what he gets is the exact copy from the original web server? How can a web master be sure that his contents are not erroneously modified? How can we find out whether there is someone who is hijacking the web content? All these questions need to be answered if we want to provide good content delivery service through active web intermediaries while reducing their side effects to the minimum level.

7.2.4 Protocol Design

Today's web content delivery protocol such as HTTP 1.0/1.1 does not consider much about active intermediaries. During the system design and implementation of such architecture, we need to think of ways to bypass some of the rigid requirements of the protocol so that both the client and the web server can still recognize the transformed request or reply. More importantly, however, there are applications that are not feasible due to the confinements or the lacking of advanced features in today's protocols. There are already content adaptation protocols being proposed to address this issue. They include I-CAP, SOAP and OPES. But to accommodate more applications into the network so that the Internet can provide better content delivery services, those fundamental protocol issues need to be addressed in the HTTP instead.

Index